Fifty Years
of
Royal Commemorative China

1887 - 1937

M. H. DAVEY & D. J. MANNION

Acknowledgements

We should like to record our gratitude to the many friends and customers whose enthusiasm spurred us on in the first place to undertake this venture, and whose continued interest in its progress has been so invaluable.

Needless to say, our families have borne the brunt of the inevitable disruption to normal home life caused by the seemingly endless photographic and writing sessions during which constant supplies of snacks, coffee, tea and biscuits were essential. Mounds of manuscripts and photographs as well as boxes of commemorative china which were "not to be disturbed" have cluttered our homes for nigh on a year! For the understanding of our wives we are sincerely thankful.

We are also especially indebted to those friends who so kindly allowed us access to their collections (often more than once) both for photography and reference. Without their assistance and co-operation this book could never have been produced. Our thanks, therefore, to Dennis Colton. Peter Gooding. Jean and Terry Higgins. Ian and Norman Holmes. Margaret Kessel. Ann and Tony King. Anne and Lisle Minns. Sue and Chris Motley. Jill and Peter Roach. Janet and Ron Smith. Christine Sbresni. Ernest Titmuss.

———— • ————

First Published in Great Britain in 1988 by
Dayman Publications
28 Box Lane, Hemel Hempstead
Herts HP3 0DJ.

ISBN 0 9513489 0 6

———— • ————

Printed by Hill & Garwood Printing Limited, Watford.
Typeset by Diamond Art and Print Limited, Watford.

Contents

Front cover: The large, hand-painted plate for Victoria's Diamond Jubilee is from the *Vienna* factory and is signed "Dietrich". The cobalt blue beaker, by *Doulton,* for Edward VII's Coronation has raised gold decoration and bears the correct date on the reverse. For George V's Coronation, *Royal Worcester* produced the pot-pourri, again all hand-painted and signed "E.Barker". The limited edition beaker from *Minton* marks the Coronation of Edward VIII.

Introduction

Dealers in royal commemoratives are constantly being asked, by collectors, to recommend a book which will tell them more about their hobby. Regrettably very little has been published which concentrates exclusively on the later ceramic items.

The aim of this book therefore is to provide an illustrated guide to the wide variety of ceramic items commemorating British royal events between the years 1887 and 1937. It is designed to help collectors by identifying pieces which they may already have in their possession or that they may still be seeking.

It was decided to cover only ceramics as it was clearly beyond the scope of a single book to do justice to the enormous array of glass, pictures, prints, textiles, tins, medals and books etc that are also an important part of the royal commemorative collecting scene. Each of these aspects would warrant a separate study of its own.

The period covered by the book, beginning with Victoria's Golden Jubilee and ending with the Coronation of George VI, can justifiably be called the "Golden Age" of royal commemoratives. More was produced, more events commemorated during these fifty years than ever before. It witnessed Britain at the peak of her Imperial power and saw the transformation to a constitutional Monarchy at the head of the British Commonwealth of Nations. It included three Royal Jubilees, four Coronations, the Boer War, the First World War and the only Abdication in British history. Many royal births, deaths and marriages were commemorated as well as a variety of tours and visits, all of which provide ample scope for collecting either generally or thematically.

One can fairly say that there is "something for everyone" in this period. To use a stock market phrase this is "the most actively traded" period for royal commemoratives.

The items illustrated in this book have been chosen from about a dozen good and varied private collections. At least three quarters of the pieces included are both obtainable and affordable with the remainder being more difficult to find and occasionally rare.

A Royal Family Tree is included which gives the dates of birth, death and where relevant marriage of members of the Royal Family which fall within the period covered by the book. Also shown are dates of conferment of Titles which we hope will be helpful in sorting out the various Dukes of York, Princesses Royal and Princes of Wales which can sometimes be a little confusing.

In order to keep descriptions as simple as possible the term porcelain has been used for those pieces which are translucent, and pottery or stoneware for all other bodies. Dimensions to the nearest half centimetre are given for the height of mugs, jugs, beakers, vases and tea ware and for the diameter of plates and bowls. Cross references are included in brackets.

In addition to Coronations and Jubilees, special sections on Births, Weddings and In Memoriams, together with a comprehensive review of pieces marking tours and visits, have been included. Five popular potteries that have gained a widespread collector following are featured in colour plates together with background notes which we hope will add to collectors' interest.

This is intended to be a guide for collectors, written by collectors and featuring collections. We trust it will go some small way to satisfy the often expressed need for a straightforward reference book.

Collecting Commemoratives

It has been said that collectors are born and not made but we strongly suspect that there is something of a collecting instinct in us all; but why choose royal commemoratives? Most of us will be familiar with the souvenirs which were given to school children at the time of a jubilee or coronation. They were rarely made of fine quality china and hardly ever occupied pride of place in the home but, nevertheless, have become family heirlooms, cherished for sentimental reasons. So it is really not surprising that, with the flood of more recent royal souvenirs on the market, an interest is rekindled. Whatever the initial inspiration, the collector will inevitably face the dilemma of what to buy next. Though it is helpful to the new collector that most 20th century commemoratives are easily identified, it may also encourage the enthusiast to buy indiscriminately, with more regard to price than quality. Every opportunity should be taken to view the range of items available and appreciate the background to this collecting field.

Royal souvenirs were made to be kept as a reminder of the event and reflected the popularity of the monarch of the day. To the modern day collector these souvenirs mean much more. They not only chronicle part of our national heritage, but represent, through their designs and inscriptions, part of our social history.

The Golden Jubilee of 1887 produced celebrations throughout the country and indeed, the Empire. Apart from the Grand Procession and Thanksgiving Service held in London, almost every town and village held their own celebrations. Children were a particular feature of the festivities. In Hyde Park 30,000 were given a tea party attended by the Queen herself, and each received a *Doulton* beaker as a memento, similar to **(32)**. At Leek, a mere 5,000 sat down to tea **(20)** and maybe less than 100 at Penmaen. **(21).**

Manufacturers were eager to exemplify the achievements and prominent events of the Victorian era in the decoration of their products. Among the most notable examples were the "Balance of Payments" plate **(31)**, the *Minton* beaker **(61)**, the Harrod's mug **(70)**, the *Alcock* mug **(69)** and the Post Office Plate **(58)**. The inscriptions and somewhat extravagant choice of words in praise of Victoria for her 1897 Jubilee make particularly interesting reading **(44)** and for the most part would be quite out of place on modern royal souvenirs.

Royal commemoratives may be regarded as an art form in their own right. Principal artists such as Robert Allen and John Broad of *Doulton* **(Cover)** and **(27)**, Keith Murray and Eric Ravilious of *Wedgwood* **(R3) (301)**, J A Robinson of *Paragon* **(248)** and Dame Laura Knight **(N6)** made contributions with their designs. Against this background the collector will quickly develop a critical eye for design, favouring one piece at the expense of another. A comparison might, for example, be made between two *Wedgwood* mugs made in 1937 - one by Keith Murray and the other pint-size one by Eric Ravilious. The latter is considered by some to be over-sized and distinctly out of place beside normal size mugs and beakers. However, the pint size mug was continued by *Wedgwood* using designs by Richard Guyatt for other royal events after 1937 and has proved to be extremely popular. The 20 or so which now make up the collection present an impressive display. Perhaps the merits of a design can only be fully appreciated when viewed as a carefully displayed collection.

Overall shapes and designs tended to be in keeping with the period. The Art Nouveau influence can be seen in **(159)** whilst the Art Deco shapes are well represented by **(215) (258) (287)**.

For the more popular events such as coronations and jubilees numerous transfers were used. Major manufacturers tended to produce "exclusive" designs, but it is not uncommon to find these used on the wares of minor potters.

The designs tested the ingenuity of the artists. For Victoria's Diamond Jubilee, designs tended to be cluttered and over-fussy. Apart from portraits, crowns, and royal coats of arms and flags, national emblems were frequently used as additional decoration, with surprisingly few daffodils in evidence! Modest collections are sometimes started by choosing just one piece for each royal event; ostensibly an easy thing to do. However, many royal events other than coronations and jubilees were commemorated, and such examples are much harder to find. A collector may feel that all is needed to round off a collection is a Queen Victoria Coronation mug. It may come as a surprise to discover that it will cost more than ten times as much as one for the Golden Jubilee of 1887.

General collections are the most popular, incorporating as many different themes as one cares to choose.

If space is at a premium the collector may have to limit the choice. Popular themes include specific manufacturers, reigns, shapes and special events.

Most collectors will either buy from dealers or at auctions. There are at present a handful of dealers who specialise in Commemorabilia selling from established premises. There are several dozen more specialists selling at antique fairs, who can be expected to carry a good and varied stock. Apart from local auctions, that might include a few pieces in their sales from time to time, the London auction houses hold regular collectors' sales.

Most specialist dealers are willing to look for particular pieces for regular customers and as a collection grows, more purchases are likely to be made this way. Nevertheless, the real joy of collecting must be in the "chase" and nothing is more likely to get the adrenelin flowing than to find a rare piece at a cheap price. Though pride of place is given to the finest pieces, collectors will always have a special affection for their bargains. Whilst bargains are still to be found, it is equally likely that goods can be over-priced by dealers who lack specialist knowledge.

It would be impossible to produce a comprehensive price guide, though some of the more common pieces will have a "going rate". The three factors which influence the value of a commemorative on the open market are quality, condition and rarity.

Quality items were produced by many of the well known china manufacturers. They would almost always be in porcelain rather than pottery, but sometimes stoneware. Particular attention would be given to design and in some cases well known artists and photographers were employed to create these designs. Extensive use was made of gilding and enamel work to embelish the background transfers. Since royal souvenirs were often displayed on shelving or mantelpieces and passed from one family member to another, it was inevitable that the condition of many of these deteriorated. They suffered chips and cracks, transfers became rubbed and gilding faded. Some manufacturers' wares were particularly prone to crazing and stress cracks. Whilst every collector is striving to find items in mint condition, they may need to be satisfied with less than perfect pieces. Particularly in the case of rarer items, more and more collectors will accept pieces which are damaged or restored. Experience suggests that a well restored item is worth about two thirds the price of one in perfect condition. The collector should always consider buying a restored piece if it enhances the collection, in the hope of replacing it with a perfect piece if the opportunity arises.

"Rarity" is a description to be used sparingly. It is surprising how many similar items come to light once the "rare" tag has been applied. Manufacturers' records are notoriously incomplete and sometimes non-existent, and often we just don't know how many pieces were made. Though the "limited edition" supported by a certificate or maker's backstamp is a comparatively modern idea, it is clear that the more expensive quality items were made in smaller numbers. These are keenly sought by collectors. Coronations and Jubilees were the most popular events and production of commemorative china was prolific to meet public demand. Other royal events were of a limited or more local interest and obviously were also made in smaller numbers. These "specials" have become increasingly popular with collectors and frequently cost more.

Ultimately the value is influenced by the three basic factors already mentioned - quality, condition and rarity. The more knowledgable collectors become the easier it is for them to judge the price they are prepared to pay to enhance their collection.

The Royal Jubilee of Queen Victoria ·1887·

After the death of Prince Albert in 1861, Queen Victoria severely limited her public and State appearances. Most of her time was spent at Balmoral or Osborne, the two homes where she had been most happy with her husband. Whilst she did, after several years of political pressure, begin to re-emerge there was still a generally held feeling that she had become too remote from her people.

Thus, the fiftieth anniversary of Victoria's reign presented a "Golden" opportunity to re-establish the links between Monarch and her subjects that had become strained over the last twenty-five years. The public had not had any pretext for royal celebrations for a long time past. Victoria did not celebrate a Silver Jubilee as it fell soon after the death of Albert; there had been no celebration of Victoria's declaration as Empress of India in 1877; royal weddings had been essentially family affairs; there had been few State visits to give rise to joyous processions. The public had been starved of events on which to lavish its enthusiasm. So the Royal Jubilee was eagerly anticipated by the politicians as a means of renewing popular approval of Victoria and by the public as a chance for a right royal celebration. The 1887 Jubilee only became known as "Golden" after 1897 to distinguish it from the Diamond Jubilee.

Since Victoria had acceded to the Throne on 20th June 1837 the Jubilee Year strictly speaking began on 20th June 1886. However, at Victoria's own request, the official celebration was to be held on completion of the 50th year. And because she did not want public festivities on the anniversary of her uncle William IV's death, the Thanksgiving Service and Procession were held a day later on June 21st. A plate by Wallis Gimson **(25)** is one of the very few items to record the 1886 date. A number of royal visits were made in connection with Jubilee events, and some were commemorated including Manchester's Jubilee Exhibition, opened by the Prince of Wales **(38)**.

Most commemoratives were transfer-printed in monochrome with a few potteries adding hand-enamelling **(13)** and others using limited under-glaze colour **(10)**. Although photography was, by this time, in widespread use so that true likenesses were generally known, the potters still produced transfers largely based on paintings. They also

1

An octagonal, pottery plate (24cms) featuring a full-length, hand-coloured portrait, maker unknown

retained great flexibility in their portrayal of Victoria. Many portraits depicting her wearing a small crown, veil and Garter Sash appear at first sight to be the same. Closer inspection will reveal wide variations in the detail of crown and sash ornaments. Two plates with similar make-up but quite different portraits are shown at **(11)**.

Many 1887 commemoratives appear relatively crude but a few do stand out as beautiful examples: the *Worcester* plate **(6)** is a striking use of a medallion profile whilst *Doulton's* Burslem wares **(32)** show a well balanced composition of young and old portraits. Their Lambeth works **(27)** are less restrained, less elegant. Whilst there is a notable lack of "impressive" pieces for 1887 there is a wealth of plates full of interesting detail **(31)**. A few municipalities commisioned their own souvenirs **(32)**, ox-roast plates **(40)** were produced and private patrons carried out their role as benefactors to the ordinary folk **(20)**.

Royal Jubilee commemoratives were produced in smaller quantities than for the Diamond Jubilee a decade later. The potters did not quite know what to expect as there had been no major celebrations since the Great Exhibition and the Crimean War in the fifties. They were better prepared in 1897.

*2 A tapering pottery mug (9.5cms) by *Doulton*. The design, by John Slater, shows portraits of Victoria at the time of her coronation and the Jubilee. This, and the slight variation shown at **(33)** is the only design produced by the Burslem factory for 1887. The mug illustrated is unusual being an example of faience ware. It has a pale green body with a dark brown transfer. Doulton Faience mark.

*3 *Minton* produced this 7.5cms pottery mug. The beautifully printed sepia portrait of Victoria framed by, "In commemoration Queen Victoria's

2   3

Jubilee 1887", combines with the ribbon above to form a pendant brooch. The town name is carefully incorporated into the design. A fine example of Minton simplicity and elegance.

*4, *5 An unusual salt-glaze, parian jug which "doubles up" for Victoria's Jubilee and the Silver Wedding of the Prince and Princess of Wales in 1888. The well moulded, relief portraits are complemented at the base by roses, thistles and shamrocks, and above by Prince of Wales feathers and fleur-de-lys as appropriate. The octagonal jug is 19cms tall and, although made by *James Dudson* of Hanley, it carries only the Registration no. 66351 on the base. Items for the 1888 Silver Wedding are quite scarce and this is the only piece that we have seen that combines both celebrations.

4   5

6

7   **8**

9   **10**

*6 A very striking pottery plate (26.5cms) from *Royal Worcester* whose printed mark appears on the reverse. The medallion portrait of the young Queen is beautifully rendered in very fine detail, (compare the GB postage stamps issued in 1840 engraved by William Wyon) and dominates the design. These plates were produced with transfer-print in blue or rose and are also to be found with a special commemoration for the City of Worcester celebrations.

*7 *8 Two porcelain cups and saucers both 7cms and unmarked. The one on the left, with printed registration no. 67299, has a very straightforward design of colour-printed flowers, "Victoria" beneath a crown and "Jubilee Year" on the saucer. The other set has a black printed portrait in an oval frame on the cup with oak leaves on the side. A crown, national flowers, "Jubilee Year 1837-1887" appear inside the rim and on the saucer. Reg. no. 65169

*9 A tapering pottery mug (8cms) which carries on the base the mark of the Bayswater Department store "William Whitely the Universal provider". Printed in brown with enamelling on the crossed flags and crown above. The ribbon contains the legend "Queen Victoria- her Jubilee Year 1887". A somewhat insipid design compared to **(10)**.

*10 A porcelain beaker produced by *R.H.Plant & Co.* This has a brown transfer-printed design of a good portrait of Victoria framed by a garland of national flowers and the date 1837-1887. On the reverse more national flowers and "for the Queen's Jubilee". A simple but effective design typical of the good quality always produced by *Plant (Tuscan China)* up to modern times. Marked RHP & Co. Reg No 63584

*11 *12 A pair of pottery plates (26cms) with different portraits of Victoria framed by the same very detailed and accurate pictures of Balmoral, Windsor, Osborne and Buckingham Palace. On the left the portrait is reproduced with acknowledgement to A. Bassano the photographers, of Old Bond Street, whilst that on the right appears to be based on a painting by Baron von Angeli commissioned in 1885 but no reference is given. Both plates bear the mark FWG and carry Reg No. 58042 and the elephant trade mark appears on **(11).** Both prints are of good quality, the left being in pale grey and the right turquoise blue.

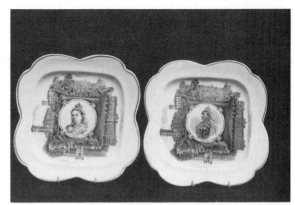

11   12

*13 *14 *15 Three examples of the fine porcelain pieces produced by *W.H Goss* whose Goshawk trademark they all bear. Goss commemoratives are characterised by their use of essentially simple cyphers which are most intricately detailed and enamelled. The Garter Sash design **(13)** appears to be less common than the "V" cypher on the other two pieces. Reg. No. 60448 is printed on beaker **(13)** whilst the other two have No. 61484. The beakers are both 10cms tall and the cup is 5.5cms. Pieces with the dates 1888, and 1889 on these designs are also to be found.

13   14   15

*16 A black printed portrait is the only decoration on the front of this small tapering pottery mug (7cms). On the reverse a framed crown, sceptre and prayer book with the date 1887 together with "England, Canada, India and Australia" in black. No maker's mark. Also seen in larger sizes.

*17 A more elaborately framed portrait also in black dominates the front of this pottery mug (9cms) On the reverse is an entwined "VR" cypher surrounded by flowers and the inscription "The Queen's Jubilee". The mug shown also has "Barcombe Jubilee Fete 1887". No maker's mark.

16   17

18   **19**

*18 The well-known "Leek" pottery mug (8cms) has, on the front, a portrait of Victoria in light brown. Made by *Malkin & Co* of Burslem (but the base is unmarked), this is one of the most elegant "local" commemoratives, with details of the special tea for 5000 scholars recorded in a delightful script on both sides of the mug **(20)** and **(22)**.

*19 This can-shaped pottery mug (8cms) has an unpretentious but striking design printed in colour. Based on a wreath of national flowers that form a frame for a "V" and crown on the front, and on the rear they entwine a ribbon with the inscription "Jubilee 1837-1887".

20   **21**

*20 One side of the "Leek" mug which details the fact that Wm. Challinor (a local solicitor) donated a recreation ground to the town which was the site of a tea for 5000 scholars. This was the high point of the celebrations and followed a procession a mile long containing over 6000 people.

*21 Another example of a local commemorative. This pottery (8cms) mug is unmarked but no doubt was produced by one of the local Welsh factories (Pleasant Vale or Llanelli). It records the "Jubilee Treat" for the Penmaen National school on the 20th June. The treatment is perhaps less elegant than the Leek mug but the "copperplate handwriting" and the directness of the statement make this a delightful piece, entirely appropriate to what must have been a very small village event. The script is printed in black on a rose coloured body. Unmarked.

*22 The third side of the "Leek" mug.

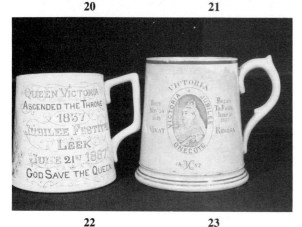

22   **23**

*23 Another pottery mug (9.5cms) produced for a local celebration, at Onecote, (a village near Leek). The front shows a portrait of Victoria in a frame containing "Victoria Jubilee Onecote", together with dates of Victoria's birth and accession. On the rear, crossed flags, a crown, 1887 and "God save the Queen". Made by *EF Bodley & Sons* of Longport.

*24 This circular pottery plate (24.5cms) has in the centre a good quality printed "mob-cap" portrait of Victoria. Dates of birth, coronation and marriage are beneath the oval frame which is surrounded by national flowers and surmounted by a crown. The whole design is in black. Backstamp of J.J Quick & Co of Handley..a retailer.

*25 An octagonal, pottery plate (23.5cms) by *Wallis Gimson*. A black, transfer print of Victoria in mob cap within the typical frame of the Gimson Company. National flowers are coloured, although other versions are

24 25

uncoloured. This plate records the commencing date of the Jubilee Year June 20th 1886. Gimson produced a large number of octagonal commemorative plates covering Royal, Political, Sporting and Religious events and personalities. Backstamps vary and often do not identify the maker. Many have the No. 41050. issued in 1886.

*26 An unusual bellarmine jug (21cms). Made of brown, speckled pottery it carries on the front a mask-head, and in a round frame "VR" and fleur-de-lys. "Great Albions Queen for fifty glorious years" encircles the middle. This unmarked jug is similar to one produced by *Doulton* but is much lighter in weight.

*27 A large (14.5cms), brown, salt-glaze stoneware jug from *Doulton's* Lambeth factory. The design, by John Broad, has a relief-moulded scene of Victoria on her Throne holding the Orb and Sceptre, with allegorical figures representing Arts, Industry, Peace and the Empire all around the jug. "Honi soit qui mal y pense" is in a moulded garter round the rim. This design appears on a wide variety of jugs in a number of sizes. Mark is impressed *Doulton Lambeth* and Reg No. 71203

26 27

*28 A pottery mug (7.5cms) with a blue transfer design, "Jubilee Year of Queen Victoria 1887" within a ribbon with a crown above and national flowers below. Maker unknown, but base has the stamp of retailer Edward Smith I.O.W.

*29 This tapering, pottery mug (8cms) has a colour-printed design including a "V" cypher, crown and dates 1837-1887. The title "Queens Jubilee" is printed in a distinctive script. Seen in a number of sizes. Unmarked.

28   **29**

30   **31**

Two octagonal plates, both 24 cms across.

*30 Has a large well-defined black portrait of Victoria in the centre. The surround is painted blue and the rim is gilt. Unmarked.

*31 Is known as the "Balance of Payments" plate. It has detailed information on the size and population of the Empire; Britain's imports and exports; and is illustrated with representative figures of Empire. This popular plate is truly typical of the Victorians' love of detail to the point of fussiness. Made by *Wallis Gimson* this design comes in finishes ranging from plain black print to versions with hand-colouring and gilding. Marked Reg No 63164 made for Silber & Fleming Ltd.

*32 *33 Two examples of the pottery mugs made by *Doulton* at Burslem. Both are essentially the same design but (33) is less common and shows a number of modifications to the original (32); the ribbon above the portraits contains "Jubilee" and is separated from them.; the crown shows some changes and is separated from the ribbon. Versions can also be found in black and sepia. This design appears on beakers given away to

32   **33**

the 30,000 children who enjoyed the tea-party in Hyde Park. The examples shown are a little unusual, bearing municipal names, a trend that had scarcely got under way in 1887. Whilst no porcelain examples have been recorded for general issue, an "all gold" beaker is reputed to have been specially made for Doulton staff.

34   35

Two examples of porcelain cups and saucers both 7cms.

*34   Is from *Wm Lowe* who produced a wide range of commemoratives until 1911. Their quality products are characterised by a design which includes a "beaded" frame for either portraits or inscriptions. De-luxe versions were raised and gilded whilst the cheaper ones were printed. This one has flags and beads hand-coloured in red and blue. Reg No 66457 (cf Plate A)

*35   Is a pretty set and, for 1887, unusually colourful. Sprays of flowers are colour-printed whilst the "V" and two roses are enamelled in red and gold. Victoria's portrait on the saucer is in purple. Mark. "Jubilee" Reg No 63310.

Retailers have played an important role in commissioning commemoratives. Whiteleys, Harrods, Mortlocks and Thos Goode, all of London, are especially renowned. Two local shops are represented here with pottery mugs specially commissioned for their respective towns.

*36   (7.5cms) has black, printed portraits of Victoria and the Mayor on either side of Lewes coat of arms. The

36   37

body is blue and the rim gilded. Marked, Buckman china warehouse Lewes.

*37   Is an intricate design in brown which includes the arms of Brighton, "Reeves Mayor 1887". On the sides framed portraits of young Victoria above "Union is strength" Mark. Cheesman of Brighton. A similar mug was made by *Copeland* for Cheesman marking George and Mary's wedding 1893 **(198)**.

*38   Manchester, as befitted a prosperous industrial city, held its own Jubilee Exhibition, opened by the Prince of Wales. This pottery plate (22cms) from *Franz Mehlem* of Bonn,

38

has pictures of the Town Hall, Exhibition Hall, Exchange and Infirmary. On each side of the Queen's head are two sailing ships; one from Manchester to Jamaica, the other to New York (fare £4.10). The design, reflecting Manchester's civic pride, is printed in brown.

39

*39 This (11cms) pottery tea-pot is ivory coloured and oval shaped. It has brown, printed cameos representing Australia, India, Canada and South Africa together with a large portrait of Victoria and on the other side the Royal Arms. This is the same print as seen on the plate in plate A. Tea-pots for the Jubilee are quite difficult to come by.

40

*40 Ox-roasts were a popular form of local celebration and this very fine pottery plate (23cms) commemorates one such event at Whittle-le-Woods. The inscription reads "an ox was publicly roasted whole on the village green in commemoration of Her Most Gracious Majesty's Jubilee June 21st 1887". In the centre a well-drawn ox is printed in brown on a cream body. Made by *S.Hancock*, Stoke on Trent

41

*41 A brown, stoneware vase (17.5cms) by *Doulton* of Lambeth has elaborate decoration. On the front, a profile of Victoria framed by laurel and a ribbon in which is "God save the Queen". The "VR" monogram is above, and on the neck "Victoria 1837-1887". On the reverse a moulded cartouche, two crowns and "The Pillar of a people's hope the centre of a world's desire". On the neck "Regina and Imperatrix". The profile and decoration is in white moulded relief and the body is speckled with gilt. Doulton and Slater mark indicates the special method used to obtain the body pattern by impressing lace into the clay during manufacture.

The Diamond Jubilee of Queen Victoria ·1897·

On the 20th June 1897 Victoria celebrated sixty years as Queen. Nine months earlier, on the 23rd of September 1896, she had also become the longest reigning monarch in British history, exceeding the 59 years and 95 days of her grandfather George III.

The closing days of the 19th Century witnessed Britain's rise to the heights of her Imperial power. Industrial, political, and social change throughout the Victorian era had progressed at a furious pace and Britain's army and navy seemed to be impregnable - the reverses of the Boer War were yet to come. And whilst there were the first signs in Europe of the tragedy to come in less than twenty years, they were no more than minor clouds in an amazingly blue sky.

Following the success of 1887, manufacturers produced vast quantities of commemoratives for the Diamond Jubilee. Many items carried vignettes depicting major achievements of the Victorian period; telegraphy, the telephone, penny post **(58)**, significant events; Crimean War **(69)**, new sporting activities **(70)**. Many showed "young and old" portraits of Victoria often with adulatory captions.

But foremost amongst the recurring themes is that of "Empire". For the official celebrations, troops from every corner of the Empire were brought to London to form the Colonial Procession. It was politicians and colonial leaders rather than European Royalty that played the leading roles. Whilst the 1887 Jubilee had been essentially family and Royal, the '97 Jubilee was clearly Imperial.

The other dominant theme was "longest reign". Many pieces included a mention of Victoria's record reign, with *Adderley* **(81)** and *Aynsley* **(72)** including the actual date of the achievement. The *Maling* mug **(57)** apparently gets the date wrong, confusing it with the 60 years reign.

Some famous potteries that had produced wares for 1887; Doulton, Goss, Wileman, Lowe etc continued for the 1897 Jubilee. Others such as Wallis Gimson and Thos Fell had meanwhile disappeared, and yet others like Hammersley, Aynsley, MacIntyre and Copeland emerged to produce quality items for 1897 and subsequent Royal commemorative occasions.

42

Designs for Diamond Jubilee items tend to be more varied and fussy than for 1887. Doulton Burslem, for example, produced only one basic design in 1887 **(32)** whilst there are a dozen or more for 1897 plus a host of colour variations **(43) (86)**. Frequently pieces reflect the Victorians' love of baroque; everything is ornate and every space filled **(42)**, **(61)**. Compare the simple medallion profile by *Worcester* **(6)** in 1887 with that of *Doulton* in 1897 **(46)**. Although colour printing was by this time widespread, most potters still relied on monochrome with added hand enamelling **(63) (78)**.
Many transfers were based on photographs. The Scottish jug **(97)** uses one by Hughes & Mullins to achieve an informal study of Victoria with the future Edward VIII. A look through contemporary magazines confirms how prevalent photographic recording of events and people had become by 1897.

* 42 One of the most detailed and attractive beakers (9.5cms) in fine porcelain from *Doulton*. The ornate coat of arms, in gold, contains a full colour portrait of Victoria. "Diamond Jubilee Celebrations" is in the ribbon below. On the reverse "VRI" in gold beneath an Imperial Crown.

43 **44**

*43 & 44 This shows the front and reverse of a pottery beaker (10cm) manufactured by *Doulton*. Transfer prints in green on a cream ground show a full length portrait of Victoria seated on a throne, holding a sceptre and orb flanked by shields showing the Royal Arms. The reverse shows the Royal Beasts, the Royal Arms and a long inscription. The inside rim has a petal decoration. This beaker can be found in a number of single colours or, more occasionally, multi - coloured. Sometimes the name of a town is printed at the base of the front.

45 **46**

*45 & 46 Another popular *Doulton* pottery beaker (10cm) shows a sepia transfer against a white background. On the front a framed "bun" portrait of the young Queen is surmounted by a crown and lion, all within an elaborate design of scrolls, roses, shamrocks and thistles extending completely around the beaker. A framed inscription reads "Victoria, the beloved Queen of England ascended the throne June 20th 1837, and by the grace of God yet reigneth, this present year of our Lord 1897". This was also produced in a number of colours and is affectionately known to collectors as "The Grace of God" beaker.

47 **48**

*47 & 48 More often than not this *Doulton* pottery beaker was commissioned by individuals or municipal authorities for presentation purposes. The sepia transfer is printed against a white ground and is less elaborate than the previous two beakers. The framed panel shows a portrait of the Queen with a simple background of a crown, flags and inscriptions. By contrast the reverse shows a circular portrait of the young Queen surrounded by sprigs of leaves. The left side of the beaker reads "She wrought her people lasting good" and the right "Given by Mrs Bartlett 1897".

Examples given by Sir Henry Doulton or H Lewis Doulton are particularly sought after.

*49 This barrel-shaped pottery mug (9.5cm) from *C.T. Maling* carries a green transfer-print of Victoria within an oval frame, supported on either side by flags and national flowers. The inscription "Commemoration Festival of Queen Victoria's Diamond Reign of 60 years June 22nd 1897" appears on both "sides" of the mug. This design is scarcer than that shown at **(57).**

*50 Victoria's portrait is set against a blue background on a pink beaded frame on this unmarked mug (8cm). Flags and national flowers either side are enamelled and the use of delicate colours creates a most attractive effect.

49   **50**

*51 A somewhat familiar but nevertheless imposing design in coloured enamels of red and blue, together with inscriptions. The reverse side of this porcelain beaker shows the Coat of Arms of Canterbury and the inscription "Presented by the Mayor of Canterbury George Collard 1897". There is a retailer's backstamp for Abrahams of Canterbury.

*52 This decoration appears on a variety of items manufactured by *W H Goss*, and in itself could form the

51   **52**

53

basis of a collection. The beaker (9.5 cm) is made of fine white porcelain on which is mounted a bold enamelled design incorporating a large crown and ribboned inscription coloured in brown and red. The letters V and R I are in pale blue enamel.

*53 This teapot (10cm) is an exceptionally fine example of a product from the *Wileman* (Foley) factory and is part of a teaset produced for the Jubilee. Matching cups and saucers, jugs in different sizes, plates and sugar bowls are also to be found. The enamelled transfer Coat of Arms is mounted on the top of the pot with sprays of national flowers to the front and rear. Both the handle and spout have some raised gold decoration with the finial shaped in a similar fashion to the handle.

54   55

*54 Tooth & Co, makers of *Bretby* Art Pottery, produced this large green pottery mug (11.5cm). Young and old portraits in relief appear on front and reverse within a frame of laurel leaves. A maker's mark and registration No 293913 are moulded in the base.

*55 A most attractive head and shoulders portrait of Victoria applied in white against a deep green ground is the only decoration on the front of this *Copeland Spode* stoneware beaker (10cm). The reverse shows a shield, again in white relief, bearing an inscription "Victoria, Queen and Empress 1837 Diamond Jubilee 1897". A number of different shapes were produced by Copeland using the same basic design and colours including mugs, teapot, biscuit barrel and jugs in five graduated sizes.

*56 Another head and shoulders portrait of Victoria is depicted on this relief moulded stoneware beaker, with dates for 1837 and 1897 on either side of the oval frame. An incised inscription on the rim of the base reads "Diamond Jubilee Holbrook Manor". The overall colour is in pale brown with a broad leaf green band around

56   57

the rim. A maker's mark for *Bourne Denby* reg No 49901 is printed on the base.

*57 In some respects the reverse of the *Maling* mug is more interesting than the front in that it records the dates of Victoria's birth, accession, marriage and jubilee. The overall transfer has been seen in green, brown, red, black and blue. An alternative portrait of Victoria was also used and again came in a variety of basic colours **(49)**.

*58 This sepia coloured plate (18.5 cm) shows the young and old portraits of Victoria. Within the elaborate design

58

an inscription records the dates of the first use of the telegraph, the introduction of the penny post and the invention of the telephone. It is often referred to as "The Post Office plate" and comes in several sizes.

*59 This pottery mug (10.5 cm) shows crossed flags and a transfer of Windsor Castle in brown. Also in brown below are a crown and inscription "In commemoration of the Diamond Jubilee of Victoria, Queen of England, Empress of India, whose reign is the longest in history". Portraits of the young and old Queen within a garland of emblems are shown on either side. There is a backstamp for Russell & Sons, Baker Street, photographers.

*60 *Burleigh* produced this shaped pottery beaker (10.5 cm) with pale

59   **60**

coloured transfers, mainly in yellow and green, against a cream ground. Names of the home countries and some of those of the Empire complete the decoration.

*61 & 62 Three sepia portraits of Victoria are combined to produce this unusual design by *Mintons*. Two separate panels print a list of the achievements in peace and war throughout Victoria's long reign and no doubt further kindled the sense of pride in Queen and country in Jubilee year.

Loyal inscriptions printed round the base and rim read "In commemoration of the glorious reign of Victoria 1837, 1887, 1897, the pillar of the people's hope, the centre of the world's desire". Mintons produced this pottery beaker (10cm) and a mug without the full inscription.

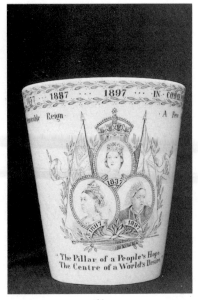

61   **62**

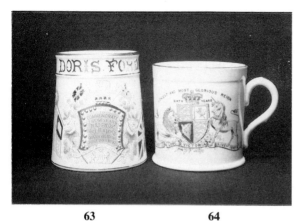

*63 The name Doris Ford in gold at the top of this pottery mug (8 cm) manufactured by *William Lowe,* suggests that this was a special presentation piece, but who she was and how many mugs were made remains a mystery. The central panel is in pale green, with an inscription in gold, framed by raised gold beading. Enamelled roses, thistles, shamrocks and flags complete the decoration.

*64 This porcelain mug is another example of the *Foley* design and is the smaller (7 cm) of two sizes.

63   **64**

The Royal Standard is enamelled in red, blue and yellow and is supported either side by a lion and unicorn. An inscription reads "Longest and most glorious reign, 60 years; long live Victoria 1837, 1897". Hand coloured sprays of national emblems decorate the inside rim. The backstamp incorporates registration number 290929.

*65 Lees Knowles MP commissioned *Doulton* to produce this jug (13.5 cm) in brown stoneware limited to an edition of 700. It was designed by W D Carol, architect for the Ecclesiastical Commissioners. The front decoration has an applied Royal Coat of Arms and date in white. A raised inscription "Fear God, honour the Queen" is set against an upper band of dark brown. Printed on the side and the back is "Remember the 60th year, the reign of Queen Victoria. The gift of Lees Knowles MP".

*66 This is a colourful art pottery waisted twin handled vase. Upper and lower incised patterns are mainly in reds, blues and greens and a yellow border contains a patriotic poem. Incised *Aller Vale* on the base with "Fred did it".

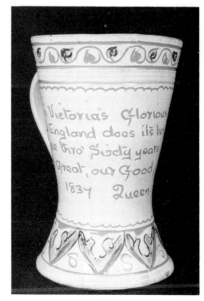

65   **66**

*67 & 68 The Victorians loved to commemorate their achievements and these two pottery mugs (both 8cm) are interesting examples.

On the left, a large sepia portrait of Victoria is surrounded by a variety of vignettes **(69)** which celebrate the first telegraph, the first steam engine, the Crimean War, as well as famous London landmarks. Made by *H. Alcock.*

On the right **(68)** is a more elegant mug, made for Harrods. A sepia portrait is again the major feature of the front but the flags, laurel leaves and flowers have some additional colour. Here the delightful vignettes **(70)** on the reverse concentrate on leisure pursuits ranging from cycling through golf, cricket, horse racing to driving of the motor car.

*71 & 72 In more sombre vein is this elegant porcelain mug (7.5 cm) made by *Aynsley* for William Whiteley, the London Department store. The front and one side are illustrated.

The all-over brown transfer-printed design has added pastel shades of blue and rose with gilding over the frame containing Victoria's portrait, on the rim and handle. Pictures of Westminster, Balmoral and Windsor Castle are included together with naval ships HMS Defence and the HMS Victory and the emblems of the Empire.

This is one of the few pieces to record the actual date of Victoria's becoming England's longest reigning monarch "The longest reign in English history Sept 23rd 1896". Also issued in pottery, with less colour and no gilding

67   68

69   70

71   72

73 74

*73 The choice of this unusual black transfer against a pale pink background is most pleasing. Victoria's portrait is framed within a circled inscription, supported by flags either side and a crown above. To the left is a seated Britannia, together with a decorated scroll and the letters VR. The other side has a similar scroll containing the inscription "A souvenir of Her Majesty's Diamond Jubilee and Glorious Reign of 60 years 1837 - 1897". The whole design is interspersed with national emblems. It is made of pottery and has no maker's backstamp.

*74 *Brownfields* produced this popular pottery mug (8.5 cm) for the city of Leicester Jubilee celebrations. The transfer shows the Queen wearing the insignia of the Garter surrounded by flags, dates and inscriptions. Parts of the body and handle are further decorated with national emblems and the complete transfer is in blue. Somewhat surprisingly, equally prominent panels either side of Victoria show the portraits of the Mayor and Mayoress of Leicester.

75 76

*75 Two examples of stoneware mugs made by *Doulton*. That on the left has a transfer print in brown against a paler background and shows young and old portraits of Victoria. A similar transfer was also used on a large jug.

*76 The other, also in brown, has relief portraits within a broad band of moulded emblems. Jugs (**F1**) beakers (**B3**) and different shaped mugs were made using this basic design, some having silver mounted rims.

*77 This large transfer printed design is found in a variety of colours including rose, green and sepia against a white ground. It was produced by *Keeling & Co* and can occasionally be found in a "de-luxe" version with enamelled flags and gold rim. The beaker (10 cm) is made of pottery.

77

*78 An attractive porcelain mug (7 cm) made by *Hammersley* which features richly coloured enamelled flags and emblems surrounding an ornate purple monogram. Both the foot and the rim have fine gold bands. The inscription reads "Victoria Queen and Empress of India".

*79 *Aynsley* collectors will recognise this design which was used on a variety of items for the Jubilee. The central scroll-edged shield and flags are enamelled in traditional colours against sprays of roses, thistles and shamrocks. The lower half of the mug (7.5 cm)

78   **79**

and handle are moulded in relief.

*80 A number of manufacturers made moustache cups and saucers to commemorate the Jubilee, and these are now particularly sought after. This *Foley* cup and saucer shows how the floral decoration on the saucer and inside the cup complement the central theme. At least two different shape moustache cups have been noted from this factory.

*81 This is an unusually pretty, light weight pottery mug (8 cm). Portraits of young and old Victoria in oval frames with inscriptions detailing

80

accession and coronation dates are repeated on each side of the mug. In the centre panel "Longest reign in English History was attained 23 September 1896". There is a wealth of pale colouring over the basic light brown print, achieving a truly delicate effect. Made by *W A Adderley,* this example has only Reg No 207000 on the base.

*82 From *Copeland* comes this chunky but beautifully designed pottery mug (8 cm). The decoration, using only pale green, is made up of panels with portraits of Victoria, Royal Arms and "60 Years of security, progress and

81   **82**

prosperity" and a commemoration of the longest reign. Plenty of detail fills the surface making this a typical product of the Copeland factory.

83   **84**

*83 & 84 The two porcelain cups and saucers illustrated here, on the left from *Wm. Lowe,* on the right by *Aynsley,* are both variants on the mug designs seen at **(63)** and **(79)** respectively. Both are high quality items with beautifully rendered printed designs embellished with a wealth of enamelling on the flags and Royal Arms.

*85 & 86 Two similar transfer printed pottery mugs (8.5 cm) made by *Doulton.* The central portrait is framed in a garland of roses, shamrocks and

thistles, with a ribbon cartouche encircling the upper part, and inscribed "Endue her plenteously with heavenly gifts, grant her in health and wealth long to live, God Save the Queen". The back inscription within a circle of leaves supported either side by cherubs, reads "In commemoration of the Diamond Jubilee of Victoria the beloved Queen of Great Britain and Ireland and the Colonies; Empress of India June 20th 1897".

85   **86**

These were made in several different colours and less frequently seen is No **(86)** showing a full facing portrait of Victoria.

*87 This compact design was used by *MacIntyre* on a number of different shapes and consists of a coloured shield of the Royal Arms, surmounted by a crown and blue ribbon cartouche with dates set against a deep cream ground. The wide gold bands around the rims of this cup (5.5 cm) and saucer add to their charm.

87

*88 Both these cups have an overall green transfer. The first (6.5 cm) is unusual in that the saucer shows a young portrait of Victoria with a coronation inscription and on its own might be mistaken for a coronation souvenir. The cup has a jubilee portrait of Victoria and the reverse shows a picture of Windsor Castle.

*89 The second (6 cm) is made by *Aynsley* to an elaborate design which is also seen on mugs and plates and in several different colours. Moulded edging to the cup and saucer adds to the attractiveness.

88   **89**

*90 Two examples of specially commissioned souvenirs. On the left, from *Doulton,* is an 8.5 cm pottery mug made for the Duke of Norfolk. On one side is a coronet, "N" cypher and "Arundel Park June 1897", on the other a crown "VRI 1837, 1897". The bold striking transfer is all in pale orange. Seen also in brown.

*91 Is a cone-shaped pottery mug (8.5 cm) on which the Arms of Bristol dominate. On one side a commemoration of the 60 years reign; on the other "Diamond Jubilee celebrations June 1897, presented by the ward of S. Augustine Bristol". Maker unknown.

90   **91**

*92 This pottery beaker (9.5 cm) was made by *Doulton* and has a green transfer on a white ground. Two opposite sides show young and old portraits of the Queen, whilst the two remaining sides have framed inscriptions beneath contemporary crowns. The unseen inscription reads "Victoria, by the Grace of God, Queen of Great Britain and Ireland, Empress of India, was born the 24th day of May in the year of our Lord 1819 and ascended the throne June 20th 1837". Doulton enthusiasts would be pleased to have this beaker in their collection.

92

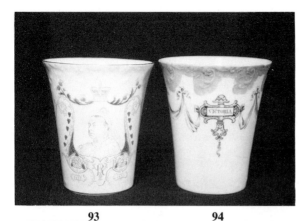

93   94

95   96

97

*93 & 94 *Crown Derby* have a reputation for producing very finely decorated porcelain and these two examples are no exception.

Both beakers have the same shaped and moulded rim, with Victoria's portrait in a shield-like frame surrounded by scrolls, roses, thistles and shamrocks. The reverse **(94)** carries Victoria's name in a simple decorated panel. The example on the left has a sepia transfer with emblems in pink, green and brown. That on the right has the overall design in blue against a white ground with the blue extended to the moulded rim. It is likely that other single coloured beakers were made.

*95 & 96 This pottery milk jug (10 cm) and the large straight - sided mug (10.5 cm) are probably both of Scottish origin. Neither bears a maker's name but the mug has a thistle mark on the base.

Both pieces have the same detailed coloured transfer of Balmoral, shown here on the jug. Printed in sepia, on the other side of the mug, is a comparatively crude portrait of Victoria framed in a spray of national flowers and an inscription "Record reign 1837 - 1897".

*97 On the other side of the jug is an interesting, and unusually informal print of Victoria with her great grandson, the future Edward VIII. The sepia print is based on a photograph taken by the Isle of Wight photographers, Hughes and Mullins.

*98 Baby plates have always been popular and those recording royal events were made by several manufacturers. The colours used on this *Carlton* plate (20 cm) are very pale, with a small central portrait of Victoria and inscription surrounded by delicate outlines of roses, shamrocks and thistles. More often than not the plates were used and examples in good condition are not so easily found.

98

*99 *Doulton* used this transfer extensively, but not exclusively, on many of their wares for the Jubilee celebrations but the quality and shape of the porcelain mug (9.5 cm) must make it one of their best examples. The rim, foot and moulded handle have been gilded. On the reverse again in gold is a cypher, crown and inscription "Diamond Jubilee 1897".

*100 It was thought at one time that this undated *Doulton* stoneware jug (19 cm) was made when Victoria was created Empress of India in 1877, but the maker's backstamp suggests a post 1891 date, whilst the portrait of Victoria is the same as that used extensively on other Diamond Jubilee stoneware jugs **(76).** Applied shields in white against brown give equal prominence to Australia, New Zealand, Cape Colony and Canada as well as India. A broad band of applied shields containing royal cyphers and crowns accompany the Royal Arms and supporting beasts. The inscription reads "Sons be welded, each and all, into one Imperial whole, One with Britain heart and soul, one life, one flag one fleet, one throne."
This jug is difficult to find.

99   **100**

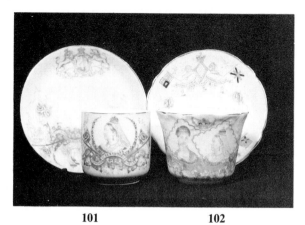

101   **102**

*101 Porcelain cup and saucer (6.5 cm), printed all over in pale blue with a portrait of Victoria framed by laurel and national flowers being the major feature of the cup decoration. On the saucer a large Royal Arms. *Longton Porcelain Co.*

*102 Another cup and saucer in porcelain (7 cm). This set has a flared cup with moulded decoration. The young and old Victoria portraits are printed in light brown but the flags have been hand enamelled. No maker's mark.

*103 & 104 Surely one of the most attractive pieces produced for the Jubilee is this dainty, square porcelain jug (11.5 cm). On one side a full colour portrait of Victoria surrounded by national flowers heavily gilded and embossed. On the other side, the colour printed and enamel design based on "VR" and flags is usually associated with Hammersley. The rim and handle are also lavishly sprayed with gold. Although there is no maker's mark this is almost certainly a product of the *Hammersley* factory. No other company produced the design at 104, whilst the portrait, so often called the "Doulton portrait", was used by other makers. The sheer quality of this piece points to Hammersley.

103   **104**

The Coronation of Edward VII · 1902 ·

Victoria died on January 22nd 1901 and Albert Edward, Prince of Wales, succeeded to the throne, in his sixtieth year, as Edward VII. Despite his widespread popularity there were many who doubted whether he would be able to take over the reigns of power from his mother and maintain the stability of the Monarchy which had been achieved by Victoria. He had been precluded by her from taking any part in the affairs of State (he was not even allowed to see the Government papers sent to the Queen), and his role had been limited, right up to his accession, to ceremonial occasions and "good works" committees. Edward had, however, kept in close touch with politicians at home and abroad through his social contacts and came to the throne far better prepared than might have been expected. He reacted strongly against his authoritarian upbringing, showing a great liking for shooting, sailing, horse-racing and the social life disdained by Victoria. Indeed she is said to have held Edward responsible in part for the premature death of Albert, as a consequence of his flamboyant, notorious way of life. Nonetheless Edward loved his family and doted on his grandchildren allowing them many of the freedoms that he himself had been denied.

Within his brief nine year reign he became deeply loved and admired at home and abroad. He worked hard at his task and his epitaph "The Peacemaker" was well deserved.

From the commemorative viewpoint the Coronation of Edward VII is interesting because the ceremony had to be postponed at the last minute, as the King had to undergo an emergency operation for appendicitis. The Coronation was postponed from June 26th to August 9th. But large quantities of commemoratives had already been issued. Thus most of the pieces seen today bear the "wrong" date. The assiduous collector will however be able to find the relatively scarce items that note the revised date. Doulton beakers (116) (117) are examples of "date postponed" and "correct date", whilst the Copeland mug (140) shows the original date crossed out and the new one inserted. Within a few months of the accession, the Boer War ended and one mug carries both the Coronation transfer and, on the reverse, a detailed picture recording the Peace proclamation (136).

By 1902 polychrome printing was commonplace and many commemoratives carried cheerful portraits of the King and Queen with a host of colourful flags and emblems. A wide selection was produced, but in general terms we see the beginning of "conformity". A lack of spontaneity seen in the Jubilee items and an overall lowering of interest in design. Some retailers still commisioned exclusive designs. Harrods and Whiteleys for example, and Thos Goode in particular developed the "limited edition" concept of expensive items produced specially for the collector.

"105 Doulton produced a number of stoneware jugs, mugs and beakers for Edward's coronation, but this particular one is less often seen than most. Commissioned by Mortlock's, it is interesting to note that the applied national emblems are similar in design to those used for the Mortlock pieces of 1887 (F4) and 1893 (K6). This jug (16 cms) has a dark brown neck and handle with the white decoration applied against a buff background.

105

106   107

*106 & 107 Both these manufacturers are popular with collectors. The first mug (9.5 cm) we have come to associate with *C.T.Maling*, the Tyneside potters **(49) (380)**. An overall green coloured transfer design shows fine portraits of both Edward and Alexandra against a background of traditional emblems and flags.

The second is a more colourful design from *R H & F L Plant* on an attractive shaped and moulded mug (7 cm). Circular portraits of Edward and Alexandra flank the Royal Standard, with a crown and enamelled flags completing the theme. The reverse has the ribboned inscription "Accession January 22nd 1901, Coronation June 26th 1902; Edward VII King and Emperor, Alexandra Queen and Empress". Other inscriptions refer to the Empire.

108

*108 Most collectors will, at some time or another, come across examples of lithophanes. This is a process whereby a shadow portrait or picture is placed within the body of the china and can only be clearly seen in front of a strong light.

*109, 110, 111 Royal lithophanes seem to have beeen confined to the coronations of Edward VII and George V **(162)** and are to be found on a number of different shapes, though cups with plain saucers and mugs are the most common with a lithophane portrait in the base. Both the cup and mug shown follow a very simple design with the royal cypher, crown and date in enamelled colours of blue, yellow and red. Sometimes other inscriptions were added, and Preston Guild and Urban District Council of Garston have been noted.

The bowl shown is a little more unusual

109   110   111

with an enamelled coat of arms, ribboned inscription and Edward's portrait in the base. Other less common shapes incorporating lithophanes of Edward and Alexandra either separately or together have appeared in a night light and decorated panels.

Queen Victoria's Royal Jubilee ·1887·

A1 A porcelain beaker (10.5 cms) by *Wm. Lowe* of Longton. The pale pink portrait of Victoria is contained within a circular frame of raised, gilded beads. Flags and national flowers are on either side of the frame which is surmounted by a crown. The beaker has a pastel blue ground and a gilded rim. The portrait version is scarcer than those with the printed inscription shown below. The beaded frame is characteristic of Wm Lowe and was used by them in 1888 **(K7),** 1893 **(K3),** for the 1897 Jubilee **(63),** and the coronations of Edward VII **(120)** and George V **(196).**

A2 One of a series of earthenware, octagonal plates (24cms) made by *Thos. Fell & Co.* The plate illustrated here is unusual in that it is printed in colour. It is more generally seen printed only in black. An interesting, well-integrating design featuring young and old portraits of Victoria, Royal Arms, and four unusual "cameos" from the Empire. They depict three hunting scenes: tiger in India, wildebeest in South Africa, kangaroo in Australia. But in Canada we are shown a cheerful toboggan scene!

A3 A fine porcelain beaker (10.5 cms) issued by *WH Goss* whose goshawk logo is on the base with Reg. No 60448. This version bears a printed "garter star" enclosing a crown, the date, a "V" and national flowers. All have some hand enamelling. "Jubilee of our beloved Queen" is the inscription on a blue frame. A matching beaker with the more commonly found design is shown at **(15).** Both transfers are found on a wide variety of mugs, beakers, vases and tea-ware.

A4, A5, A6 Three colour variants of the attractive porcelain mugs by *Wm Lowe* (7 cms). Yellow, white and rose grounds all bear the same design of a raised, gilded frame containing the inscription "1887 Jubilee Year of Her Majesty Queen Victoria. Commenced to reign 1837" Two carry, round the rim, "God save the Queen" in gilt lettering. Basic design also produced in printed version **(35)** and on earthenware items.

WM Lowe continued to produce a very wide range of commemoratives until 1911 covering all the major Royal events as well as some of the military leaders of the Boer War. This company's wares in themselves could form an interesting and comprehensive collection.

112

*112 A pottery mug (8.5 cms) with an elegant colour-printed portrait of Victoria surrounded by a wreath of national flowers also in colour. On the reverse "In commemoration of the fiftieth year of the reign of Queen Victoria, Ellel June 20th 1887". Unmarked

Queen Victoria's Royal Jubilee · 1887 ·

(see page 32)

Plate A

Queen Victoria's Diamond Jubilee ·1897·

B1 *James MacIntyre* & Co of Burslem Staffs made this pottery jug (14.5 cm) to commemorate the Diamond Jubilee. Though there is no portrait, nevertheless the deep blues contrasting with the reds, coupled with the mediaeval script come together to give a very pleasing effect. The same design was used on other shapes (87) of which a match striker is most common.

B2 No collector of commemorative wares is likely to go very long before coming across an example of what is often called the "Four Castles" plate. The maker is unknown, but it could be of Continental origin and is made of pottery. Though the basic transfer remains the same, variations in size and colouring are frequently seen. This version is larger than most (29 cm) and is, strictly speaking, a plaque rather than a plate, with holes in the back for hanging. Moulded cartouches on the rim are picked out in delicate pink with some gilding to the inscriptions. Coloured transfers in some detail show the four royal residences of Windsor, Balmoral, Buckingham Palace and Osborne House. Victoria's portrait dominates the centre of the plaque framed by roses, thistles and shamrocks. Inscriptions record the year of her coronation and Diamond Jubilee and refer to the longest reign on record.

B3 Two moulded panels in green depict young and old portraits of Victoria on this pottery beaker (13 cm) made by *Doulton*. The upper border has a dark brown band with relief moulded national emblems in white below. All of this is set against a deep blue background. This design was repeated on jugs (F1) and mugs (with or without silver hallmarked rims), and it can also be found in brown.

B4 Yet another shape bearing *Foley's* 1897 design. This tea caddy (16 cm) is both functional and decorative but so rarely found with the cover intact. The distinctive round cover has a gold rim and the top shows a transfer printed banner suspended from a ceremonial trumpet containing "An Empire, Liberty".

B5 *Aynsley* manufactured this outstandingly decorated jug (10 cm) using a similar design to that used on a cup and saucer (D7) and mug. The handle and moulded rim are heavily gilded and a picture of Balmoral Castle appears on the inside rim. One must speculate that a matching teapot was made and if indeed it were it could be a superb example of this manufacturer's wares.

B6 Small parian busts were popular at the time of Victoria's Jubilee and it is not at all surprising that quite a number were made. This pose of Victoria without a crown is less familiar than most and has been finely sculptured.

B7 The central portrait and flags used on this *Doulton* mug (7.5 cm) also appear on a sepia printed beaker (47) though the rest of the decoration has been changed. Inscriptions read "Diamond Jubilee commemorative 1897 God Save the Queen of Great Britain, India and the Colonies". Coloured national emblems appear extensively on the sides of the mug and all six flags are heavily enamelled. A special diamond shape back stamp, which is seen on other Diamond Jubilee items by Doulton, reads "Victoria R I Diamond Jubilee, Doulton Burslem". Some of these mugs were printed on the base "Manufactured for T Eaton & Co Ltd Toronto". Thomas Eaton being a well known department store in Canada. There is nothing to suggest they were exclusively made for Eatons.

B8 Teapot collectors be pleased to add this to their collection. The design is a familiar one from the *Copeland Spode* factory and was used on beakers (55) and other wares. However, the teapot's shape lends itself to a more elaborate decoration, and the spout, handle and finial are all moulded in a very pale brown which contrasts well against the dark green body of the pot. On the front the applied white portrait of Victoria is partly framed with national emblems and the inscriptions have been neatly positioned above and below the spout. It is difficult to find this teapot in an undamaged condition.

Colour Plate C. (page 37)

The Coronation of Edward VII ·1902·

C1 *Worcester* produced this porcelain plate for the city's coronation celebrations maintaining a tradition which was started for Victoria's Golden Jubilee **(6)** and repeated for George V's coronation **(181)**. The large sepia profiles of Edward and Alexandra are in a leaf frame against a background of roses, shamrocks and thistles. Cameo portraits of the Mayor and Mayoress of Worcester are shown below, with the Worcester Coat of Arms at the top of the plate.

C2 These very familiar portraits used by *Doulton* appeared on many of their wares **(114)** made in varying degrees of quality. This beaker (10 cm) is one of their finest. The white body is made of fine porcelain with the complete decoration in gold rather than the more common sepia finish. A garland inscription on the reverse is also in gold and two gold bands decorate the rim.

C3 Parian busts and figures have attracted increased interest from collectors in recent years and this example of Edward in his coronation robes is an impressive example.

C4 Miniature commemoratives can form the basis of an interesting collection but are not always easily found. *Foley* made this top hat in at least two sizes as well as a number of other reduced-size pieces. W. H. Goss were the leaders in this field **(144)**.

C5 A charming porcelain spill vase (10.5 cm) from the *Doulton* factory. Portraits of Edward and Alexandra are shown on two sides whilst the third records the coronation details within a shield supported by a crowned lion. An inscription below reads "Coronation postponed until 9th August". A particular feature of the vase is the way in which the three handles have been offset on their top and bottom mounts.

C6 Matching plates (22 cm) from *Doulton* are to be found showing these large portraits of Edward and Alexandra. A scalloped border with gold crown and cypher enhances the quality. A third plate of the same size and shape was made with portraits of Edward and Alexandra in a design and quality almost identical to that of the beaker **(C2)**.

C7 *Aynsley* made this attractively decorated porcelain cup (7 cm) and saucer. Both have raised mouldings on which the transfer and enamel designs are mounted. The Royal Arms within an inscribed circular band is similar to that used on a mug **(D5)** though the background flags are draped differently. On the inside of the cup is shown a spray of flowers and on the saucer the coronation chair of Westminster Abbey and the throne of the House of Lords. **(126)**. This idea was often repeated and can be found on coronation pieces as late as George VI. The cup shows the correct August date.

C8 This *Hammersley* mug (7.5 cms) is a larger example of that shown at **(G8)**

C9 Separate portraits of Edward and Alexandra within the gold beaded frames are shown on this richly coloured cup and saucer. The rims are scalloped and gilded to add to its attractiveness. A green shield contains "To commemorate the Coronation of King Edward and Queen Alexandra June 26th 1902" W.L.L. is printed on the base for *Wm Lowe* of Longton.

*****113** This is an unusual porcelain mug (7 cms) from *Wm Lowe* which marks the Proclamation of Edward and the Death of Victoria.

113

Queen Victoria's Diamond Jubilee · 1897 ·

Plate B

(see page 34)

The Coronation of Edward VII · 1902 ·

(see page 35)

Plate C

*114,115 Collectors of *Doulton* will be familiar with the striking half length coloured portraits of Edward and Alexandra. The portraits in various sizes are to be found either separately or together on a number of wares. On the reverse, several different designs were used incorporating the crown, royal cyphers and inscriptions with the finer porcelain examples sometimes decorated in gold (**C2**) rather than a transfer colour. The longer inscription (**117**) within a garland of oak and laurel leaves is more usually seen. Less

114   115

often seen are porcelain examples produced as special gifts and the beaker shown (**116**) was, in fact, commissioned for a John C Straker. Both these beakers bear a "correct date", and in the case of the pottery tapered-shape beaker (9.5 cm) the correction has been added below and reads "Coronation postponed until 9th August". Many shapes, including plates, jugs and small dishes are to be found bearing these portraits of Edward and Alexandra.

116   117

*118 Although the coronation had been postponed, the majority of manufacturers had already produced and sold items for the forthcoming coronation bearing the June date, and few were inclined to change the date on their transfers. It is not surprising, therefore, that examples with the correct or corrected date are scarce and generally cost about half as much again as one with the June date. The example shown is the reverse of a mug (7cm) from *R H & S L Plant*, the front of which is the same as (**107**). A rose, shamrock and thistle motif in coloured

118

transfers and enamel appear above the dated inscription.

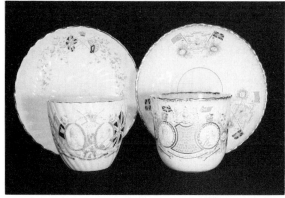

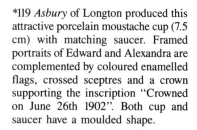

119   **120**

*119 *Asbury* of Longton produced this attractive porcelain moustache cup (7.5 cm) with matching saucer. Framed portraits of Edward and Alexandra are complemented by coloured enamelled flags, crossed sceptres and a crown supporting the inscription "Crowned on June 26th 1902". Both cup and saucer have a moulded shape.

*120 Collectors of *William Lowe* will immediately recognise this cup and saucer. The raised gold beaded frames, with portraits of the King and Queen on either side of the inscribed shield, are in a style typical of this very collectable potter. The colourful design is repeated on the saucer and enhanced by a gold rim. Included in the loyal inscriptions is a reference to Edward's proclamation on January 24th 1901.

*121 Though this beaker (9 cm) of Continental origin has no portrait, the design is nevertheless most effective. The central coloured crown is circled by laurel leaves with enamelled flags, inscription and cypher completing the theme.

*122 Egg cups commemorating royal events are becoming very popular with both egg cup and commemorative

121   **122**   **123**

collectors. The portrait of Edward in coronation robes is inscribed "His Majesty King Edward VII" but is not dated.

*123 The unmarked porcelain mug (7 cm) records the royal event in a simple but attractive way. The enamelled Royal Standard dominates the design against a brown transfer printed background.

*124 Both these items feature enamelled Coats of Arms and flags supported by national emblems. The mug (8 cm) has an inscription on the base which reads "Long life and happiness to King Edward VII and his beloved Consort Queen Alexandra". It also bears the retailer's mark for James Green of London.

124   **125**

*125 The covered porcelain pot was made by *Aynsley* and is interesting in that it shows transfer prints of the coronation chair of Westminster Abbey, the throne of the House of Lords and the Stone of Destiny on the reverse side **(126).**

Commemoratives by Aynsley

Plate D

(see page 42)

Commemoratives by Paragon

(see page 43)

Plate E

Commemoratives by Aynsley

D1 This tall porcelain mug (10.5 cm) shows a facing sepia portrait of Edward VIII in coronation robes flanked by flags and a picture of Westminster Abbey and Windsor Castle on either side. The reverse is colourfully decorated with the Arms of Australia, Canada, New Zealand, Soth Africa, India and West Indies. A similar design was used for a cup, saucer and plate.

D2 A more formal design has been used for this porcelain mug (9.5 cm) celebrating the Coronation of George V. In keeping with Aynsley tradition the decoration incorporates attractive colours and enamelling. A lion and unicorn support a shield of the Royal Arms with flags in the background. The inscriptions "Honi soit qui mal y pense" and "Dieu et Mon Droit King George V" also appear. The rim has a narrow gold band and a simple national emblem motif is on the reverse.

D3 An equally attractive cup and saucer commemorates Victoria's Diamond Jubilee. Both are extensively moulded and the rims of each are gilded. The royal Coat of Arms form the central theme surrounded by roses, thistles and shamrocks. A feature of this piece is the cluster of emblems inside the rim of the cup with a scrolled inscription which reads "For Union and Queen". All of this is repeated on the saucer.

D4 It is suprising how few quality items seem to have been made for the Silver Jubilee of King George V and Queen Mary but this porcelain mug (7.5 cm) from Aynsley is an exception. Sepia head and shoulder portraits of the King and Queen in coronation robes are separately framed with an array of flags on either side. Attractive pictures of Windsor Castle and the Houses of Parliament appear on the side panels and an inscription on the reverse reads "Empire on which the sun never sets". An appropriate silver coloured band has been added to the rim and handle.

D5 Another variation of a shield bearing the Royal Arms has been used for this Edward VII coronation porcelain mug (8 cm). Enamelled royal beasts and flags again feature and a pale pink cartouche contains the inscription "To commemorate the coronation of King Edward VII and Queen Alexandra". The fluted rim, together with the simulated rope handle add to the overall attractiveness of this mug.

D6 Loving cups were particularly popular at the time of the 1937 coronation and this delightful example from Aynsley is amongst the best produced. The portrait of George VI and Elizabeth is framed in a similar fashion to the Jubilee mug (**D4**) but the complete decoration is against a pale green background. A lion and unicorn are again in evidence as are the national emblems, including daffodils which are also repeated inside the cup. Moulded handles, rim and base are picked out in narrow gold bands.

126

D7 This porcelain cup (7 cm) and saucer commemorating the Diamond Jubilee can be found in several slightly different colours and qualities. The one shown is heavily gilded around the framed portrait of Victoria, and on the relief moulding to the rims of both cup and saucer. Pictures of Westminster Abbey, Windsor Castle and HM ships Defense and Victory are prominent and loyal inscriptions abound. An exceptiopnally fine piece.

*126 Reverse of Aynsley mug showing the Throne in the House of Lords and the Coronation chair in Westminster Abbey.

Commemoratives by Paragon

E1. Cup and Saucer (7 cms) for the coronation of Edward VIII. Both pieces are lavishly decorated with well-drawn and coloured flowers (including daffodils). An EIR cypher is over-printed. The same basic set was issued for George VI without a cypher, only the backstamp revealing it to be a commemorative piece, **(K5)** as well as one with the GR cypher.

E2. Preserve pot (7.5 cms) for the Silver Jubilee of George V. The sepia transfer of George V and Queen Mary used on most Paragon 1935 items is on the front. The handle of the lid is in the form of moulded, coloured national flowers.

E3. Loving-cup (13.5 cms) for the coronation of George VI. This large, straight sided example has gold lion handles with richly enamelled Royal Arms dominating the front. It is No. 103 of an edition limited to 500. There are three other similar limited edition versions all somewhat smaller. Two are in editions of 1000 each and one was produced in the "House of Windsor" series in an edition of only 250.

E4. Preserve pot (7.5 cms) for the coronation of George VI. Has a simplified form of the Royal Arms seen on the loving cup. The lid has a gold lion as the handle.

E5. Coffee cup and saucer (6 cms) for the coronation of George VI. One of the prettiest pieces made by Paragon. Diminutive and delicate the surface of both cup and saucer is almost entirely covered with decoration.

E6. Pin tray (12 cms) for the coronation of Edward VIII. The cypher is in pale blue in this example, also seen in gold. A wide range of pin trays, bowls and dishes were made with variations in decoration.

*127 This porcelain plate (21.5cms) is richly decorated in the typical Paragon style created by JA Robinson, cf. Edward VIII plate **(248)**. The inscription "King George and Queen Mary" is printed in sepia around the moulded rim and in the centre two cartouches, containing GV and M, are surrounded by national flowers, crown and ribbon against a background of pink and blue acanthus leaves. Interestingly, there is no date, because in fact the plate was produced in 1953 as part of the "House of Windsor" series of five plates commemmorating the 1911 Coronation, 1935 Silver Jubilee, 1937 Coronation of Edward VIII, 1937 Coronation of George VI (two plates), and the 1953 Coronation of Elizabeth II. They were made in very limited numbers and are therefore keenly sought by Paragon collectors.

*127A The photograph shows, in the centre, a group of three pin trays all of different design for the coronation of George VI flanked by two small bowls for Edward VIII again of different treatments.

127

127A

Commemoratives by Doulton

Plate F   (see page 46)

44

Commemoratives by Hammersley.

(see page 47)

Plate G

Commemoratives by Doulton

F1 A set of matching jugs 15 cm, 18.5 cm and 23 cm, was made by Doulton to this design and colour which is similar in most respects to the beakers (B3) and mugs. Green bands about the middle and neck contain inscriptions "She wrought her people lasting good" and "Dei Gratia, Victoria, Queen & Empress". The jugs were not necessarily sold in sets of three and the middle size seems to be found most often.

F2 Most of the plates produced by Doulton for the Diamond Jubilee feature the Garter sash portrait of Victoria, but this one was a special commission for the Coventry celebrations and bears the name of the Mayor of the day, Albert S Tomson. It is unlikely that this was made for general distribution and was possibly given away at a civic function. The plate is also found in red.

F3 Transfer printed portraits of Edward and Alexandra dominate the front of this jug (20 cm) with a distinct Nouveau style motif separating the panels. The body is in a pale brown with a broad dark brown band to the neck and rim. A printed inscription in a narrow band around the base of the jug records the date of the coronation.

F4 John Mortlock & Co of Oxford Street commissioned this jug (12 cm) for the Golden Jubilee. A panel in relief shows the royal cypher and crown with a cluster of roses, thistles and shamrocks symetrically placed on either side. An incised inscription reads "Mortlock's Jubilee jug" and the special retailers back stamp is on the base. This design can also be found on a loving cup but without the reference to Mortlock.

F5 Coloured examples of porcelain beakers (10 cm) for Edward VIII's coronation are very difficult to find. They were made in four ground colours - green, rose, ivory and cobalt blue. The front panel shows a colour printed portrait of Edward with a gold curtained frame. A garland of gold oak leaves decorates the inside rim. On the reverse, again in gold, is printed "King Edward VIII, God bless him crowned May 12th 1937".

F6 Though these transfer portraits of George and Mary are seen on many of this manufacturer's wares it is unusual to find them on a large porcelain loving cup (10 cm). The date, crown and cypher are all printed in sepia and similarly an inscription with the familiar leaf frame on the reverse side "Long life and happiness to King George V and his beloved Consort Queen Mary, crowned June 22nd 1911". Rim and handles are gilded.

F7 The design for this Silver Jubilee item was something of a departure from tradition for Doulton, but reflected the Deco influence of the time. Indeed similarities can be seen with contemporary table wares and, in particular, their Casino range. The angular shape and simple sepia portrait within a modern frame are not to everyone's taste. Nevertheless, a collection of mugs, beakers, pin trays and sugar bowls, (of which there were at least three with different styled handles) can make a striking display (215).

F8 For the coronation of George and Elizabeth the four coloured beakers were again produced. Portraits were by the artist Fortunio Matania and bear his signature and the design was almost identical to that used for Edward VIII (F5). An inscription in gold on the reverse reads "To celebrate the coronation of their Majesties at Westminster Abbey 12 May 1937".

F9 This is one of the rarest pottery mugs (9.5 cm) manufactured by Doulton and shows photographic portraits of the young and old Queen within medallions on either side of the handle. Though there is no date or inscription, the back stamp suggests a date prior to 1902 and after 1891. Interestingly, an almost identical design (without the Queen's portraits) was used extensively on jugs made by Pinder Bourne just before the company was purchased by John Doulton in 1876. Doulton is known to have continued to use their designs over a number of years and clearly this was resurrected some 20 or so years later. The geometric pattern to body and handle are moulded in relief and are coloured in blues and dark brown. Some mystery remains regarding the event it commemorates. It is most likely to have been made for the Diamond Jubilee though the colouring would befit an in memoriam piece.

Commemoratives by Hammersley

The colour photograph shows a representative collection of the very attractive pieces produced by Hammersley between 1897 and 1937. All are in fine porcelain and rely largely on the use of heavily enamelled Royal Arms, flags and Royal Cyphers. Rims and handles are often richly gilded.

G1 Mug (8 cms); George VI Coronation. Ornate colour transfer consists of a shield with "George VI, King and Emperor". Enamelled flags and flowers are on each side and an inscription beneath reads "acceded Dec 10th 1936 crowned May 12th 1937, long may he reign". This is one of four designs noted for the Coronation of George VI cf. **(278) (295) (296)** , and whilst each differs in detail they all demonstrate the individual style of Hammersley's rich decoration.

G2 Mug (7.5 cms); George V Coronation. A seated Britannia, printed in sepia is within a Union flag which in turn is supported by sprays of oak leaves and Royal Arms all richly painted. Inscription reads "King George V crowned June 22nd 1911".

G3 Mug (9.5 cms); Edward VIII Coronation. Enamelled Royal Arms with a distinctive cypher surmount coloured national flowers. Above are the inscriptions "Acceded Jan 20th 1936. Crowned May 12th 1937".

G4 Mug (8cms); George V's Silver Jubilee. Royal cypher in enamelled pale blue surrounded by coloured flowers and flags which are also richly coloured decorate the front of this large mug. "Silver Jubilee 1910 - 1935" and "Long may they reign" are printed in sepia. The general design approach harks back to the styles for Victoria's 1897 Jubilee **(G6)** and Edward VII's Coronation **(G9)** but there is sufficient re-arrangement of the elements to make this another very "individual" piece.

G5 Cup and saucer (7cms); Edward VIII Coronation. The Royal Arms and supporting flags are heavily coloured both on cup and saucer. The ER cypher differs from that in G3 though a set with this design was also produced.

G6, G7. Mug (6 cms). Dish (15 cms) Victoria's Diamond Jubilee. Both items are dominated by a VR cypher in rose with sprays of flowers and flags which as usual are richly hand-painted. Note the incorrect Union flag. An interesting inscription reads "Victoria Queen and Empress, 60 years honour and renown". This design is combined with a "Doulton" portrait on a beautifully shaped jug **(103)** to create one of the prettiest 1897 commemoratives.

G8 Mug (6 cms); Edward VII Coronation. Royal Arms and flags, richly enamelled constitute this fairly straightforward design. Note how it was re-used for the Edward VIII Coronation **(G5).**

G9 Cup and saucer (7 cms); Edward VII Coronation. This design evidently owes its origin to that used for Victoria's 1897 Jubilee (G6) with the cypher ER replacing that of VR.

*128, *129. Pin tray (12 cms)and mug (9.5 cms) both for the Coronation of George VI. The same basic design of crossed, hand-painted flags and national flowers is adapted to decorate both pieces. The mug has rich gilding on the rim and an especially thick handle entirely gilded.

128   129

Commemoratives by Foley/Shelley

Plate H

(see page 49)

Commemoratives by Foley/Shelley

H1 When Edward VIII abdicated Shelley were obliged to change their design for the coronation of George VI, though they retained the bunched Union Jacks, crown and lower inscription used for Edward **(H4)**. Extensive gilding has been used on the inscribed rim, base and handle to make this a fine quality piece. Portraits of the Princesses appear on the reverse.

H2 This Foley design for the 1897 Jubilee is one of the most popular with collectors partly because of the impressive way the heraldic beasts have been combined with the enamelled Royal Arms, and partly due to the large range of shapes and sizes available to the collector. This shallow dish (20.5 cm) has fluted edges with gilding to the rim and handles. A number of different sized dishes were produced and this example is one of the largest. So popular was this shape that it was used over quite a few years on souvenir ware.

H3 A particular feature of this cup and saucer produced for the Golden Jubilee in 1887 is their unusual octagonal shape. The central theme is based again on the Royal Arms which incorporates a large crown against a spray of leaves. An intricately shaped handle on the cup together with a coloured crown and trumpet on the inside rim adds to the quality. Plates, dishes, mugs, a teapot and candlestick with a snuffer, have all been seen. There is no manufacturer's back stamp but the reg. mark 64761 was a listed design by Wileman.

H4 Several dozen shapes were produced in both pottery and porcelain for Edward VIII's coronation bearing this design. A colour transfer of Edward in coronation robes is contained within a frame of bunched flags. A ribboned inscription on the top outer rim records the event and a further design inside the back rim incorporates the national emblems. The reverse shows a simple royal cypher, crown and garland of leaves.

H5 For the Silver Jubilee of George and Mary in 1935 Shelley reverted to a design first used for Edward VII **(H7)**. Colour transfer portraits of George in naval uniform and Mary are separated by an enamelled Union Jack and crown on this porcelain mug (7 cm). The event is recorded in an inscription below and again on the banner of a heraldic trumpet on the back inside rim. Cups and saucers, plates and small dishes were also made.

H6 Perhaps one of the most exquisitely designed pieces for the Diamond Jubilee is this teapot (15 cm). Though it is unlikely that they were put to every day use by their owners, it is still particularly difficult to find examples which are complete and undamaged. The design is the same as that used on the other Jubilee wares but extensive use has been made of gilding to the shaped spout, rim, handle, and finial. Familiar sprays of emblems are repeated on the lid and reverse of the pot to enhance the quality.

H7 Two different designs were made for the coronation of Edward VII and Alexandra and this one shows coloured transfer portraits of them both separated by the Union Jack and crown. Inscriptions for the June date appear on the front, whilst the back reads "King of Great Britain and Ireland and of all the British Dominions beyond the seas, Emperor of India". A crown and an ornamental lion have been added to the inside back rim. Foley were commissioned by many towns to produce souvenirs for their local celebrations. This mug has "1902 Blurton" printed on the back.

H8 For the coronation of George and Mary in 1911 alternative designs were used and this fluted beaker (10 cm) shows the non-portrait version. Yet again, an enamelled Royal Standard forms the basis of the design and is supported on either side by mythological figures. Roses, thistles and shamrocks form a background with a simple inscription recording the event. Like so many of this factory's wares, the design was repeated on a number of other shapes and in different sizes.

H9 Jugs have always been popular with collectors and this one (8 cm) is a very fine example of shape and quality. Close examination of the handle suggests that it matches the teapot. **(H6).**

*130 shows a most interesting green transfer variation on the well known "King's Dinner" beaker from *Doulton* shown in **(132)**. No doubt inspired by the success of the 1887 Jubilee children's parties, Edward initiated a "King's Coronation Dinner" for which he reputedly paid some £30,000. There were, in fact, a number of King's Dinners within the London Boroughs on the 5th July 1902, where more than half a million poor people of London sat down to dinner as guests of the King. Each was presented with a pottery beaker made by Doulton commemorating the event. Though the reverse of the beaker reads "The Kings Coronation Dinner, presented by His Majesty Edward VII" they were clearly not personally presented by the King.

*132 At the time about one million of these beakers **(132)** were manufactured and those surplus to requirements were used for other local presentations. They can be found in five colours, brown, green, blue, violet and maroon, with green being the most common colour,

*131 This is yet another example of a Continental manufactured beaker used as a memento for local celebrations. The front has brown printed portraits of Edward and Alexandra, whilst the reverse shows that of G. Frost Esq, MD, Mayor of Bournemouth, together with a Borough Coat of Arms.

*133 Retailers Diplock of Hove sold this tapered pottery mug (8.5 cm) showing a coloured transfer portrait of Edward above an elaborate design of royal beasts, flag and emblems.

*134 Royal beasts also feature on this Doulton pottery mug (8.5 cm). This particular transfer print is to be found in several colours including sepia, green and blue, and was a popular design on beakers as well as mugs. The reverse inscription reads "Long life and happiness to King Edward VII and his Beloved Consort Queen Alexandra, crowned June 26th 1902".

130

131   132

133   134

135   136

*135 & 136 This pottery mug (8 cm) was made by *Grimwades*. The front printed transfer shows portraits of Edward and Alexandra within a heart shaped frame and was used by a number of manufacturers. More unusual is the patriotic theme on the reverse depicting a British soldier and a Boer farmer shaking hands, against a background featuring a seated Britannia. The inscription reads "Peace proclaimed Sunday June 1st 1902".

*137 William Whiteley's Store commissioned this attractive porcelain cup (6 cm) and saucer made by

Aynsley (Reg 384025). The complete transfer is dark green and shows Edward and Alexandra within a frame of laurel leaves, national flowers and flags. An inscription on the reverse of the cup reads "King of Great Britain and Ireland and the British Dominions beyond the seas, Emperor of India and Defender of the Faith". Both the cup and saucer are slightly moulded and have gilt rims. The name Irthington Parish is printed on the front of the cup.

*138 Collectors soon discover that this ever popular "Dainty White" shape porcelain cup (5.5 cm) and saucer

137   138

was used by *Foley/Shelley* for commemorative and crested wares over a number of years. The enamelled transfer is that most frequently seen on Foley items to mark this event. An almost identical inscription to the previous Aynsley cup and saucer appears on the reverse.

*139 Both these pottery mugs bear the correct coronation date. The first (7.5 cm) has no potter's mark and shows coloured transfer portraits of the King and Queen with a seated crowned lion in the foreground and a reference to Neatishead School.

139   140

*140 *WT Copeland & Sons* manufactured the other mug (7.5 cm) which is printed in sepia. The June date has been blocked out with the correct date printed below. On the reverse is an ornate coat of arms entitled "Imperial Federation"

*141 Two very different stoneware beakers (12.5 cm) from the *Doulton* factory are compared here. That on the left has dark brown printed transfer profiles of Edward and Alexandra, a motif of national flowers and royal cyphers, all against the familiar pale brown body. An inscription on the reverse refers to the Thames Ditton village celebrations.

*142 By contrast, the other beaker has a moulded relief design incorporating portraits of Edward and Alexandra, roses, thistles and shamrocks in blue green and pink reflecting the Art Nouveau style, against a blue ground. Two versions of this beaker were made, one undated and the other simply dated 1902. Mugs in the same design are also seen, with or without a hallmarked silver rim.

141   **142**

*143 It was fairly common for manufacturers of household goods to produce a special royal souvenir edition of their containers, and biscuit tins are perhaps the best known examples. The Colman's mustard pot (6 cm) made by *Minton* has a brown transfer decoration with inscription.

*144 *W H Goss* produced the other pot in delicate porcelain, showing an ornate pair of initials, national emblems and crown all enamelled in green, yellow and red, with inscription below. The design is exclusive to this manufacturer and can be found on a variety of shapes in different sizes.

143   **144**

*145 Masonic items have become very collectable and this interesting inscription appears on the reverse of a blue transfer printed *Doulton* mug similar to (134). It would have been specially commissioned by the Lodge and a comparatively small number would have been made for Axminster members and possibly other nearby Lodges.

145

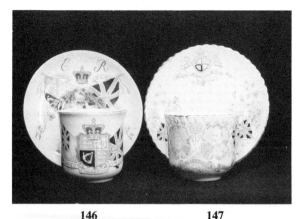

146   147

148   149

*146 Though there are no portraits on this porcelain cup (7 cm) and saucer by *Hammersley,* the bold use of a richly enamelled Royal Standard and flags make it a most attractive piece. Royal cyphers, emblems, inscriptions and gilded rims complete the decoration which is repeated on the saucer.

*147 The other cup (6.5 cm) and saucer have slightly moulded edges which enhance the transfer printed portraits of Edward and Alexandra. Sprays of roses, shamrocks and thistles, together with enamelled flags complete the decoration. Maker unknown.

*148 The pottery beaker (10.5 cm) on the left was made by the well known West Country pottery *Aller Vale.* Portraits of Edward and Alexandra in buff coloured relief are set against a dark green ground within a garland of national emblems.

*149 Framed transfer portraits of Edward and Alexandra dominate the design of this pottery mug, but the reverse is perhaps more interesting. It shows portraits of HRH the Princess of Wales and HRH the Prince of Wales (later George V) with a picture of S.S. Ophir and Federation Parliament House, Melbourne, which he opened on May 9th 1901 **(P5).** This unmarked mug (8 cm) for Edward's coronation, would have been produced after George's return from his extensive overseas tour, in November 1901, when he was subsequently created Prince of Wales.

*150 The Prince and Princess of Wales feature again on this pale orange transfer pottery mug (9.5 cm). On the front are crowned portraits of Edward and Alexandra framed in a similar fashion to that shown. The Prince and his family lived in Marlborough House at the time and it is likely that these

150

were specially commissioned coronation souvenirs for the staff and tradespeople associated with the Prince's household. The name Elizabeth Ann Weston is printed in gold on the side of the mug which was made for Harrods by *Maling.*

* 151 & 153 The front and back of these two transfer printed pottery mugs (8 cm) are shown. On the left are imposing single portraits of Edward and Alexandra with a garland of leaves with emblems. An inscription below a crown commemorates their coronation on 26th June 1902 and the overall colour is very pale red.

*152 & 154 The second shows framed head and shoulder portraits of the royal couple with the added interest of vignettes of an elephant, ostrich,

151   **152**

153   **154**

camel, moose, kangaroo, cow, lion and ships to represent countries of the Empire.

*155 Three distinct designs feature on this porcelain *Goss* tyg (8 cm). The exclusive Goss enamelled transfer **(144)** seen on a variety of items from this manufacturer appears on the one side, but equally prominent on the other two sides are the Arms of Edward and Queen Alexandra. To find all these designs appearing on one item is most unusual.

*156 A tell-tale beaded frame containing Alexandra's portrait suggests that the manufacturer was *Wm. Lowe* and this is confirmed by the backstamp. The tapered beaker is small (7.5 cm) and made of porcelain. Enamelled flags, crown and roses together with the portrait are set against a white background, which deepens to a blue tint at the base and rim. The overall effect is very pleasing . One must speculate that a matching beaker showing Edward's portrait would have been made.

155   **156**

157   158

*157 Although there are no portraits on this pottery mug (8 cm) made by *Thomas Morris,* Staffs, nevertheless this large transfer printed design in colour is imposing. The familiar Royal Standard and crown are supported either side by a rampant lion and unicorn with a background of roses, thistles and shamrocks. Suitable inscriptions complete the theme. A local inscription for St. Michael and All Angels Pirbright is printed around the rim.

*158 This is a slightly smaller mug (7 cm) with a sepia transfer showing Edward and Alexandra in adjacent oval frames with a background of national emblems. Portraits of Edward usually show him in ceremonial robes or uniform, so this particular portrait of him is somewhat unusual.

*159 *Royal Doulton* produced this jug (18 cm) to a design very similar to the beaker **(142).** As well as relief portraits of Edward and Alexandra, those of George, Prince of Wales and the young Edward (later Edward VIII) have been added. Colours are the same, but the Art Nouveau design is dominated by a rose, shamrock and thistle. Two bands of inscription read "In commemoration of the coronation of their majesties, King Edward VII and Queen Alexandra Anno Domini MDCCCCII".

*160 Souvenir ribbon plates were particularly popular at the turn of the century and were so called because they were often decorated with coloured ribbon around the outer border **(J8).** They are almost always of continental manufacture and are frequently found with a lustre finish. This colour transfer portrait of Edward fills the centre of the plate and though it is undated it would have been made as a coronation souvenir. A similar plate showing Alexandra would also have been made, and together make attractive collector's items.

159   160

The Coronation of George V ·1911·

Following the death of Edward VII on May 6th 1910, the throne passed to his second son George, Prince of Wales, who succeeded as George V. (Edward and Alexandra's eldest son Albert Victor, Duke of Clarence, **(359)** who should have succeeded had died in 1892).

George came to the throne at a difficult time; at home there was a major constitutional crisis when the Liberal government threatened to have hundreds of new Peers created to overcome entrenched opposition by the Tories in the House of Lords: the "Irish Question" soon became a highly charged political issue; and the suffragette movement was gathering momentum. Abroad the Kaiser's Germany became increasingly belligerent, whilst Austria was annexing the Balkans and antagonising Russia. Through a complex series of alliances, all the major Powers in Europe found themselves at war in 1914. Although the efforts of Edward "The Peacemaker" seemed to have come to nought there was a substantial benefit from his diplomacy in the alliances with France and Russia. And his popularity at home allowed George and Mary to take up the mantle of Monarchy secure in the affections of their people despite the tensions caused by the enormous changes in British politics and society.

Following the Coronation on June 22nd, the Prince of Wales was invested at Caernarvon on July 13th; the Fleet was reviewed at Spithead on June 24th and later in the year King George and Queen Mary received the homage of the Indian Empire at the Delhi Durbar on December 12th. The Festival of Empire at Crystal Palace had opened just before the Coronation and this event plus all the others mentioned were commemorated.

161

*161 A typical pair of inexpensive busts made in large quantities for the Coronation.

It is also worth noting that in the early part of his reign, George, by proclamation on 17th July 1917, changed the name of the Royal House and Family to Windsor. Thenceforward all German titles and honours were abandoned.

In reviewing the commemoratives issued for the Coronation of George V, one comes to the sad conclusion that there is little new or exciting in design. The potters, for the most part, were content to follow the patterns set for 1902.

Doulton continued to produce fine colour prints on their Burslem wares decipting George in military (red) or naval (blue) uniform. Foley/Shelley retained a design based on enamelled Royal Arms used in 1897 **(64)** and 1902 **(137),** although they also produced two versions of a litho design using portaits **(166) (167).** The second looks wooden and unsymathetic, Goss **(11)** and Wm Lowe **(190)** also issued derivative designs whilst Aynsley on the other hand, dropped its arms and flags approach used in 1897 **(79)** and 1902 **(125)** in favour of portraits **(172)** a style continued in 1935 **(D4)** and 1937 **(D6).**

Thos. Goode continued to commission interesting designs from Copeland both in luxury limited editions and in cheaper souvenirs **(190).** Their mug, reminiscent of 1902, makes good use of monochrome. It is one of the few pieces to use "King and Emperor". Most simply celebrate "King George and Queen Mary". The Imperial flavour has dissappeared together with most of the poetical verses etc of earlier Jubilee and Coronation items. But for the diligent seeker there are gems to be found .... just look at the charming beaker **(197),** a real piece of fantasy.

162   **163**

*162 This pair of porcelain mugs (7 cm) bear the cyphers of King George and Queen Mary respectively and contain lithophane portraits of them in the base. Lithophane examples of Edward VII are most easily found with those of Queen Mary very rarely seen. The lithophane process has been attributed to Mintons, but more recent research suggests that they were almost certainly of Continental manufacture. Although the simple cypher design seemed to be most popular, other transfers do appear on items with lithophane portraits in the base, including one from the *William Lowe* factory.

164   **165**

*164 Crowned portraits of the monarch on coronation souvenirs are not so often seen. However, several examples are to be found **(130) (181)** including this brown transfer printed pottery mug (7.5 cm) by *Booths*. The framed profile portraits are flanked by drapes and emblems. An inscription on the reverse reads "Long life and happiness to King George V and his beloved Consort Queen Mary, crowned June 22 1911".

*165 By contrast, the smaller *Crown Staffs* mug (6.5 cm) has no portraits but is nevertheless an attractive piece enhanced by a continuous band of roses, thistles, shamrocks and crowns inside the rim.

166   **167**

*166 &167 Both these *Shelley* mugs (8 cm) (7.5 cm) are popular with collectors and show two different coloured portraits of George and Mary. They are most easily identified by the way the King's hair is parted. The two different transfers are to be found on a number of items including beakers and small dishes.

*168 An attractive porcelain mug (8 cm) on which large coloured transfer portraits dominate, separated by a shield, crown and national flowers. Made by the *Ceramic Art Co Ltd* which traded for only a short time.

*169 Dates of George's and Mary's birthdays and marriage are recorded on this coloured transfer printed mug by *Star China* (Paragon). The back decoration consist of crossed Union Jacks, a Royal Standard and a maple leaf, but there is no evidence to suggest that it was especially made for the Canadian market.

168   **169**

*170 A royal cypher within a decorated circle of laurel leaves forms the basis of the coloured transfer on this porcelain beaker (8.5 cm) by *Williamson* of Longton. Small hand painted roses, a crown and a band of leaves around the rim complete the design.

*171 Head and shoulder portraits of George and Mary appear against a brown draped curtain background on this *Doulton* porcelain beaker (9.5cm). The inscription "George V crowned 1911" is on the reverse within a scrolled panel. The portrait of George can be found both in Naval (blue) and Army (red) uniform and they seem to have been equally popular.

170   **171**

*172 *Aynsley* (reg 574814) manufactured this colourful porcelain cup (6.5 cm) and saucer. Enamelled portraits, flags and emblems mostly in reds, blues and greens are repeated on both cup and saucer. Vignettes symbolising Canada, South Africa, India, Australia and New Zealand enhance the decoration.

*173 A small portrait of Prince Edward in naval uniform between those of his

172   **173**

parents adds interest to this *Grafton* cup and saucer. The transfer on the front of the cup is printed in pale rose and is repeated on the saucer.

174 175

176 177

178 179

*174 The absence of portraits does not detract from the appeal of this *MacIntyre* transfer on a jug (11 cm). A gold inscribed shield and crown are flanked by coloured enamelled flags, scrolls and emblems. Royal cyphers within a laurel leaf frame are printed on the reverse and the rim has a wide gold band.

*175 This all green transfer was an exclusive design made for Harrods Ltd, but it is similar to a multi-coloured one used by *Maling*. Patriotic inscriptions on the sides of the mug (8 cm) read "Rulers of an Empire on which the sun never sets, send them victorious, happy and glorious long to reign over us", and the coronation date has been painted on the inside rim.

*176 Collins China Store, Wisbech, comissioned this ornately designed beaker (10 cm) though there is no manufacturer's back stamp. Separate coloured portraits of George in naval uniform and Mary appear against an overall green transfer. An inscription records that 2,500 beakers were presented by the Mayor and Mayoress Mr and Mrs Weston Miller. The Wisbech coat of arms and the coronation date also appear, but we are left to speculate on the precise nature of the presentation.

*177 *Doulton* collectors will immediately recognise this head and shoulders portrait of George, with Mary on the reverse. The same portraits can be found in different sizes, either separate or together on a variety of wares from this manufacturer. Entwined cyphers, crown and date usually accompany the portraits.

*178 Both George and Mary appear in coronation robes on this colourful *Copeland Spode* porcelain beaker (9.5 cm). Flags and emblems are enamelled and an inscribed green band around the rim records the occasion.

*179 In keeping with tradition, coronation tea parties were held all over the country including one at Crystal Palace on June 30th 1911. *Doulton* manufactured a large number of beakers in two transfer colours, brown and green. Facsimile signatures appear under the portraits of George and Mary respectively for the Crystal Palace beaker. References to local events are to be found printed on many similar beakers.

*180 The *Worcester* factory manufacured a number of fine quality coronation commemoratives **(cover)** including these two contrasting plates with pale blue transfers. That on the left shows a framed rural scene and lake with Windsor Castle in the background. A simple cypher, crown and date at the top of the plate record the event.

*181 The name of the Mayor, Emmanuel Thomas, is inscribed below the municipal arms of Worcester, with the implication that this was produced

180   181

for an official celebration. The more unusual crowned profile portraits of the King and Queen give it added interest.

*182 Crowned portraits of George and Mary in coronation robes feature in this coloured transfer manufactured by *Bishop & Stonier* (Bisto) of Staffs. This pottery beaker was again produced in 1913 to commemorate their Majesties visit to Leek **(325)**. The same transfers were used but with a reference to the visit replacing that of the coronation.

*183 The same transfer portraits have been used on this porcelain mug as for

182   183

that on a *Doulton* beaker **(177)** though there is no manufacturer's back stamp. Gold decoration on the rim and shaped handle contibute to the overall quality. No inscription or cyphers have been added and one must assume it to be for the coronation. "Doris" is printed in gold at the side with Mary's portrait on the back.

*184 *Fieldings* used the same transfer as the Star China Co **(169)** for this mug. However, the pale cream body which darkens towards the rim and base is typical of Crown Devon ware. A gold handle adds to the quality.

*185 Brown transfer printed portraits, coloured emblems and flags dominate

184   185

the front of this pottery mug (8 cm). The rest of the decoration consists of vignettes of ships, royal residences and the coats of arms of Canada, India, Australia and South Africa. Registration No 57738 appears on the base, but there is no manufacturer's name.

186   187

*186 This more elaborate design in purple by *Doulton* has very similar features to one produced for Edward VII's coronation (134). An inscription records that it was a Bedgebury Park Memento, Goudhurst, Kent. The back is inscribed "Long life and happiness to King George V and his beloved Consort Queen Mary crowned June 22nd 1911" which again is very similar to the Edward VII transfer (117).

*187 An unmarked art pottery mug shows brown relief portraits of George and Mary against a cream ground. Crudely painted flowers surround the portrait. The reverse is inscribed "Borough of Poole to commemorate the coronation of their Majesties King George V and Queen Mary 22nd June 1911, H D Ballard, Mayor". There is no maker's back stamp, though reminiscent of Aller Vale (148).

*188 & 189 Both these *Doulton* mugs were commissioned by London Boroughs. That on the left (7.5 cm) was presented by Ion Hamilton Benn, MP for Greenwich and shows the borough arms and coronation inscription. The other (7 cm) bears a portrait of George like that used for the coronation dinner

188   189

(179) and was presented by Sir Walter Phillimore at a children's fete in the Borough of Kensington. The transfers are frequently found in green or brown.

*190 This pottery mug (7.5 cm) is another Thos. Goode commission from *Copeland*. The design is printed all over in light brown and consists of framed portraits of their Majesties on one side and the Royal Arms on the other with intertwined royal cyphers. "To commemorate the coronation of George V King and Emperor and Queen Mary June 1911" is on a band at the rim with "God Bless our King and Queen"

190   191

beneath the portraits. Similar in style to the one for Edward VII (140).

*191 A tapered porcelain mug (8 cm) has coloured portraits of George (in blue uniform) and Mary on the reverse. Although not dated it would have been produced for the coronation in 1911. Makers *Grafton China*.

*192 One of the joys of collecting *Doulton* commemoratives is the opportunity of finding unusual transfers, often with a very local interest. Apart from the municipal commissions, the factory undertook the production of what must have been comparatively small orders, thus maintaining a tradition first started in 1887. The front of the breakfast cup (8.5 cm) shows a pair of coloured portraits of George and Mary separated by a small crown. George is in naval uniform. On the reverse is a litho sepia picture of a billiard hall. Printed on the side of the cup, also in sepia, is a lion

192

holding a shield in which is the inscription "Gainsborough W M C & I" (Working men's club and institute) with a coronation inscription. The saucer has a standard cypher and crown.

*193 Similarly, the beaker (10 cm), shows George and Mary, with George in military uniform on one side, and a litho picture of Mouswald on the other. Though these litho specials are not often found, there were probably other examples made.

*194 Although this large mug (10.5 cm) is not made of fine porcelain, the transfer more than makes up for a lack of quality. Very few full length portraits seem to exist on coronation souvenirs and, unlike the other one seen **(1)** this shows a true likeness of the royal couple. The transfer shows them in coronation robes with Mary seated. Colours are mainly reds, blues and brown, with no retailer's or manufacturer's back stamp.

193

194

195   **196**

*195 *Grimwades* Staffordshire potters produced this mug on which all three verses of the National Anthem are recorded. The front shows coloured portraits of the King and Queen with a suitable inscription. A few years later this factory became particularly well known for its "Old Bill" wartime pieces again with a patriotic theme.

*196 For this beaker (10 cm) celebrating the coronation of George and Mary, *William Lowe* have reverted to the design used on the cup and saucer **(C9)** for Edward VII, though this example is not so lavishly decorated. Inscriptions are arranged in the same way on both items.

*197 Full length portraits on coronation souvenirs are uncommon. Though this coloured transfer is stylized in its presentation, it has a certain charm of its own. The scene is somewhat reminiscent of the etiquette to be found in Elizabethan times. There is no maker's backstamp.

*197A These fine coloured portraits are found on mugs and beakers as well as plates and were used by *C T Maling* of Newcastle. The bold clear transfer portraits, accompanying flags and intricate shield and arms in the centre contribute to its popularity with collectors. More often than not to be found combined with the Arms of Newcastle-upon-Tyne and a reference to the Mayor of the time.

197

197A

The Coronation of George V ·1911·

*J1 *W H Goss* made this fine porcelain cup (6.5 cm) and saucer for the Coronation of George V and Mary. The intricate design on both cup and saucer is cleverly based on the letters G and M and in this respect is similar to other royal commemoratives from this factory (**144**). Small panels on the letter G show animals representing countries of the Empire and a shield bearing the Royal Arms is in the centre. The letter M is set against delicately woven national emblems. The rims of the cup and saucer are gilded and extensive use has been made of coloured enamels. In the Goss tradition, many shapes were made which carried this commemorative design.

*J2 A tapering, pottery mug (9 cms) designed by *William Moorcroft* as a private commission for Mr. and Mrs. Lazenby Liberty (whose facsimile signatures are on the base). At the time, he was still working at James MacIntyre prior to setting up on his own in 1913. Moorcroft produced small quantities of commemoratives, mainly for private use (a 1902 mug for the Liberty's, another 1911 mug for Lord Norton, a 1919 Peace mug for Mrs Liberty), and all are characterised by hand-drawn lettering, muted colours and stylised floral emblems. Mugs and beakers were produced in larger quantities for the 1937 Coronation (**320**) and his son Walter continued the tradition with items for the 1953 Coronation. Moorcroft commemoratives, especially the earlier pieces, are keenly sought after.

*J3 Another example of the *Foley* design for 1911 (**H8**). Cups and saucers with this design are fairly common and this particular one uses the ever popular Dainty White shape.

*J4 Something very different from the *Royal Copenhagen* factory, though very reminiscent of their products. The porcelain plate (19.5 cm) has a two tone blue background of roses, thistles and shamrocks. A large interwoven G and M is surmounted by a stylized crown with the date in Roman numerals below. The border contains a simple geometric pattern with Latin inscription. A most attractive plate.

*J5 This porcelain mug (7.5 cm) was made by J A Robinson of Stoke who used the *Arcadian* back stamp and were particularly known for their small souvenir wares. The colour transfer is partly enamelled and shows familiar portraits of George and Mary together with emblems, crowns and coats of arms. On the reverse, within a garland of laurel leaves, is a detailed inscription which reads "Long life and happiness to King George V, born June 3rd 1865 and Queen Mary born May 26th 1867. Married July 6th 1893. Crowned June 22nd 1911 at Westminster Abbey".

*J6 *Doulton* manufactured this stoneware tyg (16 cm) which shows George in naval uniform on a front panel in brown and blue moulded relief. A similar panel on the second side shows a portrait of Mary. The third side bears a raised inscription within a shield decorated with roses, shamrocks and thistles and reads "The coronation of King George and Queen Mary 1911". The body of the tyg is in a mottled green often used by Doulton on their stoneware products. Handles are finished in dark green with a broad band around the rim. A large variety of shapes and sizes were made by Doulton using this design, including jugs, mugs, beakers, tobacco jars and tea pots.

*J7 This is an unusual and attractive mug (7.5 cm) from the *Star China Company*, who were later to be known as Paragon, and gives the taste of the quality of items which were to follow in later years. Small roses form the letters G and M with enamelled flags, emblems and crown completing the design. The reverse shows coloured transfers of crossed swords of spiritual justice and the sword of state with orb. A second pair of crossed swords represent temporal justice, together with a sword of mercy and ampulla for the coronation oil. Both the rim and base have narrow gilded bands.

*J8 One of a pair of ribbon plates (19.5 cm), this one showing George V in naval uniform. There is no date but it would have been sold as a coronation souvenir. Almost certainly of Continental manufacture.

The Coronation of George V · 1911 ·

(see page 64)

Plate J

Royal Weddings and Anniversaries

For centuries, marriages between Royal Families had been based on political grounds. The acquisition of territory or the forging of alliances were the mainsprings of choice. By the close of the 19th century the notion of territorial expansion through inter-marriage was virtually ended, nor was there much political benefit. Although Victoria's descendants were spread throughout the Royal houses of Europe, family ties did not prevent two of her grandchildren, George V and Kaiser Wilhelm, from leading their countries against each other into the First World War. In Britain, by the 1900's, Royal Weddings had become more "love matches" (albeit to "suitable" partners) than political expediencies. In view of the popular interest aroused, suprisingly little commemorative ware was produced. The 1893 Wedding of the Duke of York (later George V) is well covered but there are few items for his two sisters' weddings or for those of his children. Not until the 1970's were large quantities of wedding souvenirs issued.

198   199

*198 Cheeseman of Brighton commissioned this pottery mug (7.5 cms) from *Copeland* for the 1893 Wedding. The brown transfer shows the Duke of York and Princess May with sprays of flowers. The Arms of Brighton are on the front and an inscription round the rim.

*199 This porcelain mug (7 cms) from *Wileman* has enamelled coats of arms and flags on the front and "Royal Wedding 1893" in a ribbon below. Two anchors and a ship recall the Duke of York's association with the sea. "Happiness", a crown and trumpet are inside.

Colour Plate K (page 68)

K1 A porcelain cup and saucer (7 cms) with Reg no 6559 *(Wileman)* for the Silver Wedding of Edward and Alexandra in 1888. The printed design has hand enamelling on the coat of arms and flags of Britain and Denmark. Compare *Wileman's* 1887 piece (H3)

K2 This German-made lustre plate (17.5 cms) marks the 1893 Wedding of George and Mary whose sepia portraits are entitled HRH the Duke of York and HRH Princess May. Photographers Russel & Son are acknowledged.

K3 A porcelain cup and saucer (7 cms) has the inscription "To commemorate the marriage of their RH the Duke of York, Princess May July 6th 1893" in a pretty heart-shaped frame of raised, gilded beads. Made by *Wm Lowe* but unmarked.

K4 A cream, pottery beaker (10 cms) from *Doulton*. On the rim "To commemorate the Wedding of Princess Mary with Viscount Lascelles at Westminster Abbey" The initials M and L within interlocking ovals, and "February 28th 1922" are printed in sepia.

K5 A metal beaker for the 1923 Wedding of the Duke of York and Lady Elizabeth Bowes-Lyon. Few ceramic items were produced and we know of none with both portraits. Hence this one non-ceramic example.

K6 A brown, salt-glazed stoneware jug (13.5 cms) from *Doulton* has white moulded national flowers on each side of an oval containing G and M. "1893" is below. Commissioned by Mortlock. See also 1902 jug (105)

K7 A pink-ground, porcelain beaker (10.5 cms) from *Wm Lowe* has the sepia inscription "In commemoration of the Silver Wedding of Their Royal Highnesses the Prince and Princess of Wales. Married March 10th 1863" in a pale yellow frame. Flags of Britain and Denmark complete the design.

200   **201**

*200 This cone-shaped pottery mug (9 cms) has an attractive black printed design based on a horseshoe entwined with mayflower and surmounted by Prince of Wales feathers. The inscription reads "Marriage of the Duke of York and Princess May July 6th 1893". Unmarked.

*201 *Doulton* produced this straight-sided pottery mug (9 cms). It has a sepia transfer of George and Mary framed by mayflower. "Royal Marriage 6th July 1893" are in ribbons above and below the portraits which are titled HRH Duke of York and HSH Princess May. On the reverse, sprays of may and roses. Also seen as beakers and barrel shaped mug.

*202 This large pottery mug (11 cms) has two excellent black printed portraits of the Prince and Princess of Wales on either side of the mug. Whilst it is not dated the apparent age of the Prince and Princess would indicate that this was issued to commemorate the Silver Wedding of Edward and Alexandra in 1888.

*203 Another undated pottery mug (9 cms) bears a sepia portrait of the Duke of York in civilian clothes. This piece was issued at the time of the Duke's marriage in 1923 to Elizabeth Bowes-Lyon. Very little was produced for this event despite the popularity of the wedding. At the time, of course, there was no indication that the couple would reign as George VI and Queen Elizabeth. A pottery jug featuring a portrait of Lady Elizabeth Bowes-Lyon issued for the wedding has been recorded; and an ash tray with the same portrait of the Duke of York was also produced.

202

203

Royal Weddings and Anniversaries

Plate K

(see page 66)

The Silver Jubilee of George V · 1935 ·

(see page 70)

Plate L

The Silver Jubilee of George V · 1935·

The reign of George V was punctuated by a series of crises at home and overseas. He came to the throne as preparations for the first World War were getting under way and by his Silver Jubilee year, it was clear that another major conflict was imminent. After 1918, old alliances and Royal family connections had broken down, and Europe was, by 1935, poised for fundamental social and political upheaval.

Britain's Imperial relationships had also been drastically altered. The Irish Home Rule Bill became law in 1921, and consequently the style "United Kingdom of Great Britain and Ireland" had been deleted from the Royal titles in 1927. In 1931 the Statute of Westminster removed direct power from the British Parliament over the Commonwealth countries and there was increasing pressure for self-government in India.

At home, in the years following the War, women demanded greater freedom and equality with men. The Reform Act of 1918 and the Equal Franchise Act in 1928 gave the vote to all women over 21. In 1924 Ramsay MacDonald headed the first Socialist government thereby changing for ever the old pattern of British politics. The rise in Trade Unionism, the General Strike of 1926, the economic depression of the 30's and the disillusionment of a populaton which had not seen its post-war dreams realised, all conspired to create continuing social and political unrest. The British people were happy to celebrate the Silver Jubilee of their popular King and Queen but were unable to ignore, for long, problems both domestic and international.

Commemoratives issued for the Jubilee, like those for his Coronation, lack for the most part, any great distinction. *Hammersley* **(214)**, *Aynsley* **(D4)** and *Shelley* **(H6)** continued to produce good quality items and *Paragon* now offered a selection of wares. The *Star China Co.* had produced a mug in 1911 **(196)** with the brand name *Paragon*, but not till 1935 did the company create its more familiar quality range.

Many designs used litho portraits of George and Mary wearing coronation robes. *Doulton* however showed them in more informal pose **(217)**. Their shapes are "deco" as is the jug **(209)** from *Masons*. Although most potteries avoided Imperial or grandiose themes, the *Crown Devon* mug **(222)** highlights notable achievements of the reign and shows the Empire on two hemispheres. And *Aynsley* re-use a theme first seen in 1897 **(71)** of "Empire on which the sun never sets".

1935 saw the introduction of the "Official Design" from the Pottery Manufacturers Federation **(223)**. Though prosaic, it was widely used and was the fore-runner of similar designs right up to 1977. Limited editions from *Copeland* continued to appeal to the collector, but one famous name - Wm Lowe had gone. Ouss had changed ownership and produced no more of their traditional pieces. And Doulton issued only one limited edition design from their Lambeth works.

Colour Plate L (page 69).

L1. A large (15 cms) de-luxe, porcelain loving cup from *Paragon*. Its front decoration of sepia portraits, flowers and flags, together with the design of Royal Arms on the reverse are more elaborate versions of those used on most Paragon wares **(204)**. There are additional inscriptions on the sides of this piece: "Souvenir of twenty five years gracious reign"and "Crowned in Westminster Abbey June 22nd 1911" Inside the rim is "To commemorate the Silver Jubilee". There is lavish gilding on the rim, base and handles, whilst on the base is printed "Replica of loving cup approved and accepted by members of the Royal Family, to commemorate the Silver Jubilee of Their Majesties Gracious Reign AD MCMXXXV"

204   205

206   207

208   209

*204 A fine porcelain loving-cup (9 cms) from *Paragon*. On the front, sepia portraits of Their Majesties are contained within oval frames of blue laurel. National flowers, Royal Arms and Union Flag, a ribbon with "H M King George and H M Queen Mary" are all printed in full colour. On the reverse is a large Royal Arms and round the rim "To commemorate the Silver Jubilee of their gracious reign 1910-1935" in red on a yellow ground. The handles are modelled as national flowers. This design appears on a large variety of items in different sizes and qualities.

*205 A rich, deep blue background with decoration in gold makes this porcelain mug (9.5 cms) one of the most elegant produced for the Jubilee. The portraits are in light brown within frames of enamelled green laurel. On the reverse, crossed flags and a crown in gold. Designed by Lucien Boullemier whose signature is beneath the King's portrait. Marked *Maling*. Newcastle upon Tyne.

*206 This pottery mug (8 cms) bears a commonly used transfer printed design. A complex mixture of portraits, coats of arms, flags and wreaths makes it a colourful and typical piece of its time. Marked *Sheppards* of Wimborne

*207 *Shelley* specially produced this can-shaped, porcelain mug (7 cms) for the Urban District of Chadderton whose arms in rich enamels form the front decoration. On the reverse "Long live the King George and Queen Mary". Inside-a trumpet, crown and "Silver Jubilee 1935". A similar mug was commisioned for 1937.

*208 This elaborately decorated pottery jug (19 cms) is one of two shown here from the *Masons* factory. Designed by Cyril Shingler in a limited edition. The front has a relief moulded profile of George surrounded by green laurel. The spout has a large hand-painted Royal Arms whilst the handle is in the form of a lion.

*209 There is a "deco" feel to this yellow-ground pottery jug (12.5 cms) The spout, handle and moulded ridges are all trimmed with silver lines. The profile is the jug's only decoration. Made by *Mason*.

In Memoriams

Plate M   (see page 74)

The "Proposed" Coronation of Edward VIII · 1937 ·

(see page 75)

Plate N

In Memoriams

M1. Several manufacturers produced plates commemorating the death of Edward VII and this is one of the more tasteful. A head and shoulders portrait of Edward in coronation robes is shown within a daintily decorated hexagonal frame. Inscriptions refer to Edward as the Peacemaker and give the dates of his birth and death. The plate is made of good quality pottery but has no manufacturer's name.

M2 *Doulton* produced this in memoriam stoneware jug (20 cm) for Victoria and it is now a comparatively rare item. The body is in mottled green with a Nouveau-style decoration in relief and coloured mainly in brown and purple. A narrow brown frieze at the base has interspersed roses, shamrocks and thistles. The framed profile of Victoria on the front is different from the more familiar one used for the Diamond Jubilee. Two raised panels either side of the handle are inscribed "Born 1819, Ascended the throne 1837, Died 1901" and "Victoria, Queen and Empress".
John Broad, who was a principal designer and sculptor for Doulton, also produced a salt-glazed figure of Victoria seated on her throne and dated 1819-1901.

M3 This pottery plaque (16 cms) shows the same portrait of Victoria as that on the *Doulton* jug **(M2).** The white profile has been finely modelled and contrasts well against the terra cotta background. Incised inscriptions read "Born May 24 1819, RIP Died Jan 22 1901". There is no manufacturer's mark.

M4 Moustache cups and saucers are in themselves keenly sought after by collectors, but to find an in memoriam one for Victoria is somewhat exceptional. *Foley* made this cup (8 cm) and saucer in fine porcelain. It shows a portrait of Victoria framed by purple drapes and flags, and suitably inscribed. The design is repeated on the saucer.

M5 Yet another rare item from the *Doulton* factory. The Garter sash portrait of Victoria was extensively used by this manufacturer for the Diamond Jubilee, so it is not surprising to find it repeated four years later. Victoria is framed by a heart shaped wreath of purple flowers. Two inscriptions are on either side of the handle. **(366)**

210

M6 An identical design to M4 has been used on this *Foley* cup (5.5 cm) and saucer for Edward VII's death. The fluted cup and saucer is in the Dainty White shape and has the usual gilding to the rims and handle. The inscription on both pieces reads "May 6th 1910, King, Statesman, Diplomat, Peacemaker".

*210 A treacle-brown pottery jug (18 cm) showing a relief moulded portrait of Victoria framed within an inscription "In memory of our beloved Queen". The reverse has a relief moulded shield with a harp, shamrock, rose, three feathers and dates for Victoria's birth and death. A reference is also made to her sixty-three years reign. There is no maker's mark.

The "proposed" Coronation of Edward VIII ·1937·

N1. This very elegant porcelain plaque (14.5cms) comes from the *Bovey* pottery.It has a striking profile of Edward in gold set against a cobalt blue background. Around the edge, in gold on a white ground, is "Coronation of His Majesty King Edward VIII May 12th 1937"

N2. Musical commemoratives have now become very collectable, and this impressive example which plays ;"God save the King", is a large pottery tyg (17 cms) from the *Carlton Pottery* of Smith & Barnett. The piece is lavishly decorated all over with hand-painted emblems etc. On the front a moulded profile of Edward; On one side "May 12th 1937" on the other "Coronation of ER long may he reign". A dove of peace, national flowers and a sheaf of wheat complete the unusual design.

N3. This Queen's ware mug (12 cms) from *Wedgwood* was designed by Keith Murray. A moulded relief profile and crown are on the front making this a simple but attractive piece. Alternative treatment with a printed portrait of Edward similar to that for George VI shown at **(R3)** was also made.

N4. There are two interesting features about this pottery cup and saucer (7.5 cms) from *Stanley* china. First is an inscription "Proclaimed Jan 23rd 1936. Abdicated Dec 10th 1936" making this one of the rare abdication pieces. And secondly, the handle moulded in flag form makes this otherwise ordinary decoration into something a little different.

N5. The "ER" shaped handle again distinguishes this attractive porcelain mug (9 cms) made by *Windsor* china (CWS). Made in several sizes, and matches those made for George VI **(289).**

N6. An elaborate design by Dame Laura Knight RA decorates this pottery mug (8 cms). Many factories used this decoration and a slightly smaller variant of it. Most are of pottery but examples in porcelain sometimes with extra gilding are to be found. The bold design featuring the King's profile, St. George and the Dragon and an elephant on the front and a large Royal Arms on the reverse is very distinctive indeed. It was simply adapted for George VI **(311).**

N7. A well-moulded head of Edward creates this interesting toby jug (11 cms) from *Bretby.* It is made of pottery and has an E shaped handle at the rear. Produced in several sizes.

N8. Again it is the handle in the shape of a flag which forms the main interest of this pottery cup and saucer (7 cms) from *Burleigh Ware.* A sepia printed portrait decorates the front and on the reverse is a cypher and date.

*211. A colour printed transfer of Edward surrounded by coloured flags is the central decoration on this pottery loving-cup (12 cms) from *Royal Doulton.* This particular transfer of Edward is not recorded on any other Doulton piece. On the reverse "Crowned 12th May 1937" in sepia with a printed cypher, crown and "Long may he reign". Interestingly this loving-cup uses the same mould as that for the "Royal Exemplar" piece for the death of George V **(370).** The base colour here is biscuit and the decoration in blue. Not often seen.

211

Royal Tours and Visits

Plate P

(see page 78)

Royal Births and Anniversaries

(see page 79)

Plate Q

Royal Tours and Visits

P1 There is no back stamp on this plate (18 cm) but the transfer was used by several manufacturers for the coronation, including *Royal Doulton* **(280)**. Two gold bands decorate the inner and outer rims and a simple inscription records Their Majesties' visit to Knottingley on October 21st 1937.

P2 It is understandable that, with the strong ancestral links a section of the population had with Wales, Edward Prince of Wales should be warmly received on his Argentinian tour of 1925. The plate (19 cm) would have been locally commissioned but was made by *William Adams & Sons* of Stafford. The coloured transfer shows a somewhat poor likeness of Edward with the inscription "Principe de Gales, 1925".

P3 Particularly pleasing to find a mug (7.5 cm) commemorating a very local visit which is in good quality porcelain and thoughtfully designed. Separate portraits of the Duke and Duchess of York are shown with a crown and flags above. The inscriptions record the royal visit to Pudsey on April 24th 1928 and that it was presented by Councillor Simeon Myers and Mrs Myers. Credits are given to Vandyk for the photographs of the Duke and Duchess, and the mug was manufactured by *J. H. Cope* (Wellington China) and retailed by W. Ellis of Bramley.

P4 This pottery mug (7.5 cm) is not often seen and commemorates a visit made by the Duke of Gloucester to Australia in 1934. The blue transfer shows a half length portrait of the Duke and is suitably inscribed below. The reverse bears an inscription advertising "Viceroy" Tea!

P5 Although Victoria's portrait appears on this *Doulton* beaker, Edward had already ascended the throne when this event took place. The occasion was the opening of the first Federal Parliament in Australia and the Duke and Duchess of York were despatched as the King's representatives at the ceremony. The beaker (9.5 cm) was made in both pottery and porcelain and is found either in sepia or green. Other items bearing the same design include teapots, jugs, plates and jardinieres.
Victoria's profile is part of an elaborate design flanked by an Australian and a British soldier. The reverse is equally detailed and shows framed portraits of George and Mary, together with those of Lord Hopetown and Sir Henry Parkes. An inscription, which is believed to refer to the help received from Australia by the British during the South African war, appears below.
Examples of these commemorative pieces are very difficult to find and are much sought after by *Doulton* enthusiasts.

P6 At first glance this is the fairly common mug (6.5 cm) made for Edward VII's coronation, but the inscription on the reverse commemorates a visit by Edward and Alexandra to open the docks at Avonmouth, Bristol, on July 9th 1908. Makers's mark for *Royal Doulton* on the base.

P7 *Aynsley* made this porcelain mug (7 cm) to commemorate the opening of the Federal Parliament House in Canberra by the Duke and Duchess of York in May 1927. The enamelled colour transfer shows a kangaroo flanked by the Australian flag and Union Jack, with inscriptions above and below. The reverse shows a coloured transfer picture of the Federal Parliament building and the date. Handle and rims are outlined in gold.

Royal Births and Anniversaries

The photograph shows a selection of the very popular birthday and souvenir pieces featuring the two daughters of the Duke and Duchess of York (later King George VI and Queen Elizabeth). The *Paragon* designs were issued on a variety of mugs and beakers as well as on tea and coffee sets of differing shapes and qualities.

Q1, Q2. An octagonal tea-plate (16 cms) and a tall mug (9.5 cms) are two porcelain pieces from *Paragon* issued in 1926 to mark the birth of Princess Elizabeth. The two magpies featured were reputed to have flown around the house at the time of Elizabeth's birth. The caption "Two for joy" (part of a nursery rhyme "one for sorrow.....") is included beneath the birds. Backstamp "For HRH The Duchess of York for Princess Elizabeth".

Q3. This can-shaped porcelain mug (7.5 cms) also from *Paragon* celebrates the birth of Princess Margaret Rose in 1930. The pretty design shows a pair of budgerigars perched on sprays of heather and marguerites and roses. Special backstamp gives date of birth and the permission of HRH The Duchess of York.

Q4. *Grafton* china produced this attractive barrel-shaped mug (8.5 cms) in porcelain with a sepia print of both Princesses. Made about 1937, the photograph is one of the Marcus Adams series.

Q5, Q6. A small cup and saucer (65 cms) which matches the coffee pot below and an oval sandwich plate (19 cms) are two further examples of *Paragon's* "budgerigar" design for the birth of Princess Margaret Rose. The plate is in ivory-coloured china with a gold rim, whilst the coffee-set pieces are in white with blue edging.

Q7. Cup (7 cms), saucer and plate (16 cms) by *Paragon*. This delightful trio issued in 1928/29 features a sepia portrait of the young Princess Elizabeth which is captioned "Our Empire's little Princess. Born April 21 1926"

Q8. The elegant *Paragon* coffee-pot (19 cms) which matches the set above beautifully shows off the budgerigar design to stunning effect.

Q9. This porcelain cup and saucer (7 cms) from *Paragon* features Princess Margaret Rose as a baby of 18 months - two years old. The black printed portrait is "signed" Marcus Adams and there is a backstamp with date of birth and permission of HRH Duchess of York. Probably issued in 1932

Q10. Both princesses apppear on this tall mug (9.5 cms) produced by *Paragon* in 1934/35. The portraits are in sepia with blue and gold trim. Dates of birth for both Princesses are detailed on the reverse.

*212. This pottery mug (9 cms) from *Doulton* marks the birth , in 1894, of the future Edward VIII. He was the first child of the then Duke and Duchess of York (later George V and Queen Mary). The same portraits were used as on the wedding commemoratives (201) printed in brown, with inscriptions "In commemoration of the birth of a Son and Heir" Borough of Richmond Surrey"

212

The Coronation of George VI · 1937 ·

Plate R

(see page 81)

The Coronation of George VI ·1937·

R1. This (10.5 cms) goblet from *Paragon* carries their standard decoration on both front and back. However this shape is rarely seen and there is more than usual gilding on the rim and base.

R2. *Copeland-Spode* produced this impressive (14.5 cms) pottery tyg to a commission from the Clothmakers' Guild. The front has very pretty sepia-printed portraits of the King and Queen. The sides have Royal cyphers, crowns and oak leaves all in gold, whilst there is a gold frieze round the rim with dates and crowns. A similarly-decorated bowl was also produced.

R3. Keith Murray designed this attractive Queen's Ware mug (12 cms) for *Wedgwood*. The front shows pale blue profile portraits of Their Majesties and there is a cypher and crown on the reverse. Moulded portrait versions were also produced to a Murray design for both Edward **(N3)** and George, whilst **(307)** shows a different interpretation of this portrait.

R4. A coloured transfer print of the King and Queen, also used by Royal Doulton **(280)** decorates the front of this porcelain loving-cup (9 cms) from *Collingwood*. Two Marcus Adams portraits of the Princesses are on the reverse **(317),** and there is an enamelled crown inside.

R5. This porcelain cup and saucer (6 cms) from *Paragon* is unusual in that there is no obvious commemorative indication on the design, only the backstamp reveals it to be a 1937 Coronation souvenir. However this design of colourful national flowers was used for Edward VIII items suitably overprinted with a cypher **(E1)** and similarly for George VI.

R6 & R7. Two unusual examples of porcelain wares from *Royal Doulton*. The tall loving-cup (12.5 cms) has profile portraits against a turquoise background framed by purple and ermine robes. The rim, handles and base have gilding. This transfer is an unusually elaborate version and is reminicent of that used rarely for Edward VII **(130)**, and more frequently for George V **(178)**. The matchbox holder (7.5 cms) bears the standard version of the portraits with flowers and coronation regalia. **(303).**

R8. A typical example of the many pintrays made by *Shelley*. The sepia portraits framed by coloured flags is the design most commonly found on Shelley wares for this event. As always the standard of printing and quality of porcelain distinguishes the wares of this manufacturer.

*213 A characteristic product from *Crown Ducal* is the pottery jug (14 cms) with geometric deco shape and decoration in red and blue on a white body. The Royal cypher is in blue and gold with the year 1937 on the reverse.

*213a This tall, porcelain mug (10 cms) from *Windsor* china features the Marcus Adams Royal family photograph on the front. On the reverse are the names of the family.

213   213A

214

*214 A fine quality porcelain loving cup (10 cms) from *Hammersley*. Transfer printed in light brown with enamelling on the flags and "GR" cypher, the design includes a ribbon in which is "King George V and Queen Mary acceded May 6th 1910 Crowned June 22nd 1911." Rim, handles and base all carry silver lining. On the reverse an orb and sceptre against a background of roses. This design was used on teaware, mugs, beakers and pin-trays. Always delightfully executed, Hammersley has become one of the "collectable" potteries.

*215, 216, 217. Three examples of the wide range of items made by *Doulton* at Burslem. The pin-tray (9.5 cms), mug (7.5 cms) and sugar basin (6 cms), all porcelain, carry sepia portraits of the King and Queen in mufti. The feeling of these pieces is distinctly "deco" with geometric shaped handles on the pot and dish and the portraits framed by straight lines. Handles are often colourful, the basin's is red and the dish has gold. Doulton wares were often overprinted and the mug illustrated is for Little Hallingbury. Bases are marked Doulton and "Silver Jubilee of Their Majesties King

215   **216**   **217**

George V and Queen Mary. 1910-1935".

*218 This waisted, pottery mug (9.5 cms) is all-over blue with "Silver Jubilee King George V and Queen Mary 1910-1935" incised into the body in black. Typical of much Devon ware this example, made for Instow, comes from *Baron of Barnstaple*.

*219 An interesting flag handle distinguishes this pottery mug (8 cms). It has an ivory coloured body with sepia portraits in green laurel wreaths, bedecked with flags. In a ribbon below is "King George V - to commemorate Their Silver Jubilee-Queen Mary".

218   **219**

Windsor Castle and the Houses of Parliament flank the portraits. On the reverse, emblems of Empire and "Empire on which the sun never sets". (Aynsley used the same design). Marked with Burgess & Leigh's trade mark and *Burleigh* ware.

*220 This pottery teapot (13 cms) is decorated with one of the most widely used transfer prints. Brown portraits of Their Majesties are set in oval frames bedecked with flags and national flowers. On each side a warship and biplane mark the progress of the Navy and Airforce by 1935. In a ribbon below "Silver Jubilee of King George V and Queen Mary". On the reverse the Royal Arms supported by "N Zealand, India, Canada, S Africa". Marked *CWS*

*221 The same design as the teapot decorates this tall, tapering pottery mug

220

(10 cms) from *Beswick*. The geometric shaped handles on this and the mug alongside again give a period feel to the pieces.

*222 A very detailed and colourful design, full of interest, decorates this pottery mug (8 cms) from *Crown Devon*. The World Map shows the British Empire in red and a number of historic events of the past twenty five years are commemorated; "Queen Mary" launched, "Royal Scot" - American Tour, Sydney Harbour Bridge built, the Schneider Trophy, First wireless broadcast etc. The

221   **222**

marriage and Coronation dates of George and Mary are also included. The reverse shows the Royal Arms and flags.

*223 A colour transfer print of the King and Queen in profile, surrounded by flags, national flowers and a ribbon with the dates 1910-1935 is the design produced by the British Pottery Manufacturers Federation. It was used by a very large number of potteries. The Federation has produced "official" designs up to the Silver Jubilee of our present Queen Elizabeth.

*224 A more interesting printed design on this pottery mug (8.5 cms) from

223   **224**

Wagstaff and Brunton consists of Their Majesties, wearing crowns, in oval frames of laurel with Britannia in between. "Silver Jubilee 1910-1935. Long live their Majesties" completes the decoration. On the reverse crossed flags, with the silver on the rim and handle.

*225 Medallion portraits of the King and Queen in sepia form a simple but striking decoration on this pottery mug (9 cms). A lion and unicorn supported by the Royal Standard are on the reverse. The treatment is reminiscent of the Doulton Burslem design for 1902 **(132)** and the Booths wares for 1911 **(164)**. This piece has no maker's mark but on the base is "George and Mary 1910-1935 Silver Jubilee".

*226 Joshua Tetley & Sons, the brewers, commissioned this 12 cms pottery waisted tankard. Medallion style portraits in blue are on the reverse

225   226

227

Anno Domine MCMXXXV".

*228 The same colour-print decorates this can-shaped pottery mug (7.5 cms) in white "royal vitreous" as was seen on the teapot **(220)** and mug **(221)** Made by *John Maddock & Sons*

*229 This pottery mug (7.5 cms) from *Grimwades* has a variation of the design shown on **(206)**. Here the portraits are smaller and the design does not cover the whole of the surface. "Bassano copywright" can be clearly seen under the shields. Mark *Royal Winton*. Grimwades

and on the front the commemoration details as seen, together with Royal Arms and "Beer is Best". The body is biscuit coloured with silver on the rim and base. Mark; *Causton* London

*227 A large, oval porcelain plate (35 cms) produced by *Paragon* carries a variation of the design illustrated on the loving cup **(L1)**. The plate also has the facsimile signature of the designer J.A. Robinson. On the reverse "Produced in the twenty-fifth year of the Gracious Reign of their Majesties King George V and Queen Mary as a souvenir of their Diamond Jubilee".

228   229

230   **231**

232   **233**

234

*230 Two examples of porcelain tea-cups and saucers both 6cms. On the left an unusual *Paragon* piece. The design consists of printed multi-colour sprays of national flowers around the inside edge of the cup and rim of the saucer. Each spray is captioned "British Isles, India, Australia, N Zealand, S Africa" as appropriate. Maple leaves form, with "Canada", the framework round the rims. In the centre of the cup an "E" made up of flowers. Marked *Paragon (China) Ltd* "Empire design. Period Silver Jubilee".

*231 On the right a cup and saucer from *Thos. Kent* uses the "Bassano" design already illustrated. The design fits the proportions of the set very well.

*232 An attractive, porcelain pintray (14 cms) from *Hammersley.* The brown, printed design with added hand enamelling is a variation of the one seen on the loving cup **(214),** though here the rim is gilded not silvered.

*233 A circular, pottery ashtray (11 cms) from *Shelley.* Colour printed portraits of George and Mary separated by a Union Flag are set within the bowl. The rim is silvered. This design appeared on a a wide range of 1935 Shelley commemoratives in both pottery and porcelain.

*234 This is another example of a commissioned piece by *Thos. Goode,* the Oxford St. retailer. A barrel-shaped, pottery mug which has three-quarter length sepia portraits of George and Mary within oval frames of laurel. "The Silver Jubilee" stands above with a crown. On the reverse the initials GR and MR with 1910-1935. Silver rim and handle decoration. As with all Goode's special pieces whether at the luxury end or, as in this case, at the cheaper end of the market, their designs are elegant and distinctive. They continue to look good today.

The "proposed" Coronation of Edward VIII ·1937·

Within a few months of his Silver Jubilee celebrations, George V died at Sandringham on 20th January 1936. He was succeeded by his eldest son, the Prince of Wales who took the title of Edward VIII. As Prince of Wales, Edward had travelled officially and privately to all corners of the globe. He had visited countless factories, mines, potteries, shipyards, commercial concerns and community projects of all kinds. He was immensely popular and was regarded as someone who could understand and sympathise with the man-in-the-street.

As the Heir Apparent, he had unparalleled experience of all levels of society and as an officer in the Grenadier Guards he had seen at first hand the horrors of war in Europe. His preparation for succession had been more thorough and broadly based than any previous British monarch. Whilst George V had gained widespread love and admiration, it was with a very definite sense of "hope for the future" that everyone turned to his popular son Edward.

The *Copeland* mug (262) perhaps best exemplifies this feeling. He was clearly "new generation". His upbringing and attitudes had not been dominated by Victoria as had his father and grandfather. Alas the hopes of early 1936 were soon dashed, for by the end of the year the crisis over the question of whether Edward was to be allowed to marry Mrs. Simpson, an American divorcee, had resulted in the King's Abdication on December 10th 1936. His younger brother, Albert, Duke of York succeeded him as George VI.

Large quantities of commemorative items had already been produced in anticipation of Edward's coronation before the Abdication was announced. Whilst local municipalities, schools and other "patrons" gave away souvenirs bearing the George VI commemoration and not that of Edward, there was nonetheless a great quantity of Edward VIII items already in circulation. Thus, although he never was crowned, its not true to say as one so often hears that Edward pieces are "rare". There were probably fewer items issued but there are still ample numbers of both 1937 coronations to be found.

Of special interest to collectors are those pieces which were either overprinted with the Abdication date (254) or were produced later with a full explanation (265). These are scarce and eagerly sought after. There also seems to have been quite a vogue for loving cups in 1937. More were issued than for any previous coronation. Whilst most of the designs are technically very competent, the availability of good colour transfers now being well established, they are also pretty conservative and predictable. A rather lonely portrait of Edward surrounded by coloured flags seems to be the favourite motif.

However, there was some attempt to add interest by producing unusual handle shapes, using initials (N5), with a flag (N8), whilst both *Copeland* (262) and Laura Knight (225) incorporated lions as did *Paragon* (261). It is also noteworthy that with rare exceptions the use of jingoistic themes and references to Empire had fallen away. The transitional phase from King-Emperor George V to King and Head of the Commonwealth of George VI was underway.

235

*235 An Artstone, bronzed bust of Edward as Prince of Wales in 1925. He is seen wearing military uniform with the rank of Major. Signed L. Jennings.

236   **237**

238   **239**

240   **241**

Two examples of porcelain loving cups produced for Edward VIII's Coronation and then adapted for George VI.

*236 is 7.5 cms and from *Samuel Radford*. It has a three quarter profile of Edward printed in brown on a blue background within a frame of laurel and multi-coloured flags. Underneath the caption "HM King Edward VIII crowned May 12 1937". On the reverse "E" crown and "Long may he reign". Pretty handles have moulded and printed crowns.

*237 (8 cms) has a more formal portrait of Edward in military uniform, printed in dark brown with a frame of laurel and coloured flags. Same design on the reverse. Rim and handles are decorated with national flowers and gilding. Marked *Sampson Bridgwood* Anchor china.

*238 An interesting pottery mug (8.5 cms) from *Beswick*. The body is ivory coloured, ribbed and carries typical Beswick relief moulded decoration which is hand coloured. (The George VI adaption appears without added colour.) Rim, base and handle have blue lining.

*239 Thos Goode commissioned this elegant, tall (10 cms) pottery mug. The black portrait sits within a blue frame supported by lions and national flowers. On the reverse "ER" and "Accession Jan 20th 1936" Gilding on base, rim and handles.

*240, *241 *Shelley* produced both the two handled pottery vase (12.5 cms) and the fine porcelain can mug (7 cms). Decoration is essentially the same on all Shelley pieces for Edward's coronation, consisting of head and shoulder portrait in coronation robes framed by laurel and flags. On the reverse of the loving cup however, there is an intriguing inscription "Tak hod an sup lad" (Say it out loud!)

*242, *243 This pretty porcelain cup and saucer (7 cms) on the left is typical of the high quality decoration produced by *Grafton China*. The sepia portrait is surrounded by coloured flowers and supported by rampant lions. The crown has hand enamelling. On the reverse "Coronation May 12th 1937". The other set comes from *Sampson Bridgwood*. It is in fine porcelain (7 cms), has deckled edges to cup and saucer, with the same decoration as on the loving cup shown at **(237)**.

*244 *Hammersley* produced this tall, (9.5 cms), porcelain mug. As with all their wares, the Royal Arms and flags are heavily enamelled, with the cypher and inscription printed in light brown.

*245 This scarce Abdication porcelain mug (9 cms) comes from the *Royal Staffordshire* Pottery. On this example the word "Proposed" has been over-printed on the front above the original "Coronation May 12 1937 inscription. Inside printed in light brown, "Abdicated Dec 10th 1936". Examples of Abdication commemoratives are much sought-after by collectors and are now hard to come by.

*246 is another unusual piece. A small (7 cms) pottery mug made by *Manley Fox,* whose mark is on the base. It shows the Proclamation being read at the Royal Exchange (one of three places in London where this ceremony takes place). All the figures are in full colour, and on the reverse is another herald.

*247 A brown printed portrait surrounded by coloured flags and national flowers which have added enamelling decorate the front of this porcelain mug (8.5 cms) from *RH & SL Plant (Tuscan China)*. On the reverse are fleurs-de-lys "Coronation May 12th 1936" *Tuscan* continue to produce fine quality pieces right to the present day.

242   243

244   245

246   247

248

*248 A large (34 cms), oval porcelain plate from *Paragon*. The richly detailed design by J.A. Robinson is based on beautifully enamelled Royal Arms. The border is moulded and carries the inscription "Edward VIII King and Emperor", a cypher in gold, and "Crowned May 12th 1936". Clusters of hand coloured fruit complete the rim embellishment. This design was reproduced on a wide range of *Paragon* items with varying degrees of gilding and elaboration.

249   250   251

*249 *250 A porcelain can mug and tea plate (16 cms) are representative pieces of a delightful range of commemoratives made by *E Brain* whose *Foley China* mark is on the bases. These depict the State Coach (with one occupant) drawn by a team of four greys, and followed by a lone horse guard and a mysterious foreign gentleman on foot with two train bearers. All the figures are hand coloured. The plate has an open landau with four persons. There is no indication of whether these were made for Edward or George. "Long live the King" would suggest Edward. Real childlike, fantasy pieces.

*251 One of the most delicate and delightful colour portraits of Edward in crown and robes is the sole decoration on the front of this pottery (10 cms) beaker from an unknown maker. On the reverse a crown on a cushion with crossed sceptres.

*252 This cream-coloured, pottery mug from *Grindley* is unusual in that it is one of the very few pieces to show Edward wearing the State Crown. The colour transfer is completed on the rim by a ribbon of brown laurel and the reverse has "ER VIII" and crown.

252   253

*253 *Bovey* pottery made this can-shaped pottery mug (7.5 cms). It has a medallion in brown on a blue background surrounded by laurel and flags.

*254 This porcelain cup and saucer (7 cms) is an example of how *Tuscan* (Plant) overprinted their coronation piece with the details of the Abdication. On the cup the quote "Abdicated 10th Dec 1936" is placed at the rear underneath the date of the Coronation. It is similarly repeated on the saucer. Front decoration as **(247)**.

*255 The pottery mug (8 cms) by *Wilkinson* has a specially adapted version of the Laura Knight design. At the rim is the inscription "Abdicated Dec 10 1936" whilst opposite the handle "Proposed" has been printed vertically. Both are in blue to match the original inscription.

254   255

*256 A striking portrait of Edward in black on a blue background is the feature of this pottery beaker (11 cms) from *Wedgwood* of Tunstall whose Unicorn mark is on the base. He looks unusually sombre in this simple but highly effective transfer. Also on mugs.

*257 A much grander approach is taken by *Royal Doulton* on this porcelain beaker (9.5 cms). Edward is here seen three-quarter profile wearing his coronation robes. He is framed by an elaborate cartouche of royal emblems and laurel all in colour.

256   257

*258 *Crown Ducal* made this impressive, large (18 cms) pottery tyg. The very "heavy" pattern of geometric squares in red, blue and white is typical of this famous factory where Charlotte Rhead had such an influence. The tube-lined decoration of the Royal cypher is elaborately intertwined. A crown in blue is on the reverse. The ornate double arched handles are lined with red blue and gold. Similar designs in brown and white have been noted on a range of decorative ware.

258

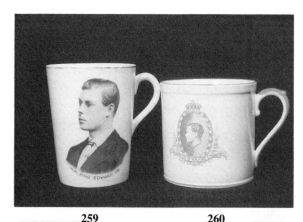

259   **260**

*259 This tapering, pottery mug (9 cms) has an unusual brown printed portrait of Edward in civilian clothes. More reminiscent of pieces made when he was Prince of Wales. The large, well-drawn transfer fits the shape of the mug most elegantly and the caption "HM Edward VIII" fits comfortably under the portrait. Maker. *Morley Fox & Co.*

*260 *Royal Staffordshire* pottery made this porcelain can mug (7.5 cms). It is an excellent example of the simple but effective use of monochrome. The portrait of Edward in a frame of laurel is printed in an attractive rose. Handle, rim and base also have rose lining.

261

*261 Typical of the wide range of products from *Paragon* China is this fine porcelain loving-cup (10 cms). It has a white body and the moulded lion handles are painted brown. The Royal Arms are printed in full colour whilst the inscription "Edward VIII King and Emperor" in white on blue ribbon surrounds the rim. On the reverse, is a union flag within laurel leaves and flags. This basic design was used extensively on loving cups, mugs, beakers tea-ware, plates etc. Many have minor variations which have their specialist "collector appeal"

*262 Another example of a Thos Goode commission, this very interesting pottery mug (8 cms) is from *Copeland*. The very detailed transfer print in full colour shows an idealised Edward in Coronation robes standing in front of a montage of mines, potteries, dockyards, warships and liners together with a representative collection of his subjects. A very "aspirational" scene. "To commemorate the Coronation of Edward VIII King, Emperor May 12 1937" is round the rim. The lion headed handle is decorated with laurel. One of the most interesting pieces for this event.

262

263 264

*263, *264 This photograph shows the front and reverse of a pottery beaker (10cms) from *Fieldings "Crown Devon".*

The body is beige with the head and crown in relief moulding. The inscription which runs round the rim is in gold and reads "Edward VIII ascended the throne Jan 20 1936 Abdicated Dec 10 1936" This and two thin red and blue lines on the base are the only colours giving a dramatic simplicity to the beaker.

*265 Yet another abdication piece (but they really are scarce!). This one is from *Hammersley*. Shown is the reverse which has a long inscription detailing the circumstances of the abdication, length of reign and accession of George VI. This barrel shaped mug (9 cms) has on the front the standard portrait print issued by the British Pottery Manufacturers Federation **(266)** and here seen on the pottery beaker (11 cms) made by *Adams*.

265 266

267 268 269

*267, *268, *269 Illustrated here are three typical pottery pieces to show just how good the transfer printing had become by this time even for the "cheap and cheerful" souvenirs. All have very decorative full colour transfers with different portraits of Edward, all swathed in floral decoration and flags, The cup and saucer is unmarked as is the egg cup whilst the mug which has a very shapely handle, is from *J Kent*.

*270, *271, *272 Three more examples from the range of pieces made by *Paragon*. On the left the reverse of a tall mug with brown painted handles (9.5 cms) has a colour transfer of a Union flag surrounded by flags. The front is shown on the chocolate cup which has a gold handle (9.5 cms). The lid in front has the "ER" cypher design which is sometimes found on the reverse of mugs, beakers, loving cups etc instead of the Union flag motif. In the centre is a particularly impressive loving cup (10.5 cms). It has a large Royal Arms on the front with much

270   271   272

enamelling and gilding. There is also an inscription inside the rim "Edward VIII King and Emperor". This is No. 134 of an edition limited to 1000.

*273 Another fine porcelain loving-cup (11.5 cms) this time from *Shelley*. The waisted shape and the elegantly bowed handles make this a very pretty piece indeed. The sepia portrait and coloured flags transfer is common to all Shelley pieces for Edward's Coronation. On the reverse, a spray of roses, thistles, shamrocks and, unusually, daffodils.

273

*274 This pottery plate (23 cms) is one of the few pieces made to mark the Accession. It has an unusual full-colour picture of Edward wearing an Admiral's uniform. The accession date 21-1-1936 is on a blue ribbon beneath the colour portrait which is surmounted by "HM King Edward VIII". Made in Belgium.

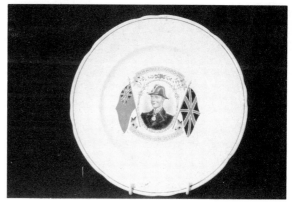

274

The Coronation of George VI ·1937·

Albert Frederick Arthur George second son of the then Duke and Duchess of York (later George V and Queen Mary) was born on the 14th December 1895 at York House in the grounds of Sandringham. Throughout his early years Prince Albert, essentially a shy person, had always played second fiddle to his elder brother Edward although they shared many experiences as cadets and naval officers together. His natural shyness allied to a severe speech impediment conspired to make "Bertie" much happier away from the limelight.

He was created Duke of York (the traditional title for the Monarch's second son) in 1920, and was married in 1923 to Elizabeth Bowes-Lyon, daughter of the Earl and Countess of Strathmore. They were a very popular couple and began taking a fuller role in Royal activities culminating in the World Tour of 1927 in which they opened the New Federal Parliament Building in Canberra. The tour was a huge success and marked the turning point for Albert's confidence as a Royal representative.

The Abdication of his brother came as an immense shock to Bertie and at the time there was grave concern as to whether he was strong enough to take over as King. However, despite some political preference for his younger brother, the Duke of Kent, he did become King and, as is now well known, with the stout support of Queen Elizabeth, overcame his shyness to become a well liked and astute sovereign, seeing Britain through the traumas of the Second World War, and the immensely difficult years of post-war change.

The May 12th 1937 date proposed for the coronation of Edward VIII was retained for that of George VI. Similarly most of the potters retained designs originally intended for Edward, and hastily carried out whatever adaptions were possible in the short time available. Some were very simple eg. Hammersley **(295)** and Paragon **(314)**. But those based on portraits now had to accommodate a Queen consort as well as the King. **(237)** vs **(276)** The Copeland mug **(290)** commissioned by Thos Goode lacks the style of its Edward original **(262)** although the portrait of Elizabeth, taken by Vandyk in 1926, is delightful. The "aspirational feel" has gone together with the title King-Emperor. The two princesses, Elizabeth and Margaret Rose, were included on many pieces **(294)** and the Marcus Adams photograph of the Royal Family appeared on a very large number of wares **(285)**. Certainly a great deal was done to promote the Royal "Family" image, something which had been impossible for Edward and now in the troublesome times after the Abdication seen to be vital in "establishing" George VI and Elizabeth.

Although there was little that was really "new" for George VI's Coronation at least one piece was original; the tyg which commemorated "1936 Year of the Three Kings" **(319)**. And for the collector there is a very interesting selection of portraits, often of the couple as Duke and Duchess of York in the twenties and frequently from Court photographers Vandyk, Bassano and Marcus Adams.

*275 From *Copeland* comes this delightful pottery mug (8.5 cms) which features a family group taken by Marcus Adams. The colour transfer also shows Windsor Castle and Westminster. On the reverse is a coronation inscription and flowers decorate the handle.

275

276 **277**

*276 This porcelain loving-cup (8 cms) by *Bridgwood Sampson,* (Anchor china), is a simple adaption of their Edward VIII piece to include portraits of George and Elizabeth. Decoration same as **(237)**

*277 This is one loving-cup (8 cms) which looks as good from the front as from the back. On one side is a G and E cypher in a cartouche of colourful national flowers and surmounted by a crown. "Long may he reign" and the coronation date are printed in brown. On the other side a printed St George and the Dragon in a frame of ribbons and flowers over a blue cypher. Around the rim in gold "Long Live Their Majesties". The handles are moulded with coloured flowers. Made in porcelain by *Adderley.*

*278 *Hammersley* produced a wide variety of commemoratives for the 1937 Coronation, but many of them were straight adaptations of those already issued for Edward. This porcelain mug (9.5 cms) is typical. The "G R" monogram is gold printed and the flags are richly enamelled. The flowers are colour-printed and the inscriptions "Long may He reign" and "Acceded

278

Dec 10 1936 George VI King and Emperor Crowned May 12 1937" are gold printed. The handle, base and rim are all gilded.

*279 *Minton* do not issue many commemoratives, but when they do their wares are always amongst the most attractive. This beaker (10.5 cms) of trumpet shape in very fine porcelain is, again, an adaptation of the Edward design. **(Cover).** Beautifully rendered portraits of George and Elizabeth in colour, within stylised floral frame and inscription all in gilt make this a very desirable piece. The thick gold band inside the rim has a repeated pattern

279 **280**

of crowns and 1937. Limited edition 2000.

*280 This porcelain beaker (9.5 cms) from *Royal Doulton* is of interest in that it it has a transfer that was also used by other potteries **(R4).** Doulton's decoration was usually exclusive.

*281 *Crown Staffordshire* made this pear shaped, porcelain mug (8cms) which has sepia printed portraits within beaded frames and coloured flags. A band of green, moulded laurel encircles the top of the mug. National flowers and a cypher are on the reverse. The portraits are by Vandyk, one of the foremost court photographers, and are frequently used **(289)**.

*282 Very effective use is made of the relief-moulding technique on this pottery mug (9 cms) from *Burgess & Leigh* (Burleigh ware). The body is ivory-coloured including the profiles,

281   **282**

283   **284**

only the laurel wreath is painted green. Simple and striking.

*283, *284 *Paragon* produced these two porcelain mugs (7 cms) and there are two further designs in the "series" illustrated as loving-cups **(304)**. The Union flag and Royal Arms are, in typical Paragon manner, most richly enamelled, whilst the rest of the design is printed in full colour. Both have pale blue handles. The reverse of each differs; on the left is a harp with shamrocks and on the right a royal cypher. This "blue handle series" is comparatively scarce.

*285 The decoration on this pottery cup and saucer (7 cms) is one of the most popular photographs of the Royal Family. It was taken by Marcus Adams who also took many photographs of the Princesses **(298) (381)** which were often used on the commemoratives from 1930 onwards. Unmarked

*286 A fine quality sepia transfer with hand-enamelling on the supporting flags make this porcelain cup and saucer (7 cms) from *Tuscan* china a very worthy example of the continually interesting commemoratives from this maker. This is another "re-design" of an Edward issue **(254)**.

285   **286**

287 **288**

*287 There is an evident "deco" look to this distinctive pottery vase (13 cms) by *Wadeheath*. The colour transfer is the same as that on the Doulton beaker **(280)**, and on the reverse is a small print of Princess Elizabeth. The cream body is enlivened by bold use of red, white and blue on the spout, base and on the triple "O" handle.

*288 This is an example of the simple yet elegant pieces made by *Burleigh Ware* with careful use of relief moulding and limited use of colour, **(282)**. This large (16 cms) pottery loving cup has moulded portraits in white on a black ground.

The cypher, frame and handles are gilded. On the reverse, a cypher in gold and "crowned May 12th 1937"

*289 The "G R" handle is the distinguishing feature of this tapering mug (9 cms) in porcelain from the CWS *(Windsor china)*. The dark brown "Vandyk" portraits in a frame of laurel and coloured flags decorate the front with a cypher in a blue frame on the reverse. Red, white and blue lines are on base, handle and rim. See Edward version at **(N5)**.

*290 Thos Goode commissioned this pottery mug (9 cms) from *Copeland*.

289 **290**

The pale brown portraits are framed by acorns, oak leaves and thistles (no roses, or shamrocks) and flags in colour. This design lacks the sheer panache of its Edward pair **(262)**. Elizabeth's portrait is again by Vandyk but taken in 1926 when she was still Duchess of York.

*291 This biscuit colour, barrel-shaped mug (10.5 cms) is one of at least two stylish designs from *Grays* pottery. The Royal Arms in chocolate brown are on the front whilst the reverse (illustrated) has an attractive cypher, crown and date all in brown. "Dieu et mon droit" on the rim and "Coronation of King George VI and Queen Elizabeth" on the base with gold lines complete the design.

291 **292**

*292 From another famous name specialising in pottery pieces - *Ridgway* - comes this waisted mug (11 cms) with excellent moulded medallion profiles and "King George VI Queen Elizabeth Coronation May 12 1937" The mug has over-all treacle glaze with silver on the rim and handle.

*293 A porcelain can mug (7 cms) from *Aynsley*. This one has a colourful transfer print of Their Majesties on a blue background and surrounded ·by coloured flags and national flowers. On the back are six shields and "The Empire on which the sun never sets". This is a re-arrangement of the design used in 1935. For different portraits used by Aynsley see **(300)** and **(D6)**. There is a crown and cypher on the handle.

*294 Another popular version of the Royal Family is printed in black on a deep blue ground on the front of this pottery mug (8.5 cms) from *Wedgwood & Co* of Tunstall. Whilst it lacks the dramatic starkness of its Edward equivalent, it is nonetheless very attractive and has become very sought after, as have most of those pieces which feature the Princesses.

*295 *296 These two porcelain cups and saucers (7 cms) illustrate the attractive "variations on a theme" produced by *Hammersley*. Both pieces are based on the use of heavily enamelled Royal Arms. The type of print used is different and the one on the right, pattern No 2435, is not so

293   **294**

295   **296**

richly decorated, but does usually include daffodils in the floral emblems. On the left, pattern No 2436, has richly painted flags as well as the Arms. Both are outstanding examples of hand decoration.

*297, *298 This pair of matched porcelain plates (26 cms) comes from *Shelley*. They are beautifully printed in colour and amongst the finest produced for this Coronation. The two sets of portraits are those used by Shelley on their commemoratives. Marcus Adams photographed the Princesses, and George and Elizabeth are again the work of Vandyk.

297   **298**

299   **300**

*299 A small, porcelain can mug (5 cms) from *Goss China* has the front filled with light brown profile portraits framed by laurel and coloured flags. A royal cypher is on the reverse. Quite different from, and less distinctive than, the commemoratives produced by this company prior to its take-over in 1934 by Cauldon potteries.

*300 This larger (7.5 cms) porcelain mug from *Aynsley* has light brown portraits of Their Majesties framed by laurel leaves and enamelled flags. A lion and unicorn support on either side. On the reverse a throne from the house of Lords. The handle and rim are decorated with national flowers and daffodils.cf. **(293)**

301

*301 *Wedgwood* began their series of commemorative pint tankards (10 cms) in cream-ware in 1937 for the "Coronation" of Edward VIII. The series continues to this day-the latest in 1986 for the conferment of the Dukedom of York on Prince Andrew. Eric Ravilious designed both mugs for 1937 - they only differ in the "G R" for "E R" and the colour of fireworks and bands at the bottom of the mugs. The one shown has red fireworks over

a black Royal arms and a green lowerband, (the other mug for George VI has a blue band).

*302 This very detailed sepia print of Hill Top Chapel and Sunday School in Burslem is on the reverse of a pottery beaker (10 cms) from *Royal Doulton*. (Could Doulton staff have formed a part of the congregation here over the years?)

*303 The porcelain mug (8 cms), alongside, shows the standard front decoration of George VI commemoratives made at the Burslem works. The profile portraits are on a blue background surrounded by flags

302   **303**

and flowers with the Coronation regalia beneath. A wide range of items in pottery and porcelain was produced with this transfer.

*304, *305 These two cream-bodied porcelain loving-cups (7.5 cms) from *Paragon* complete a series of four designs - see **(238)** for the other two. On the left the cypher and the date in blue are within a turquoise wreath. A crown and flags all hand enamelled surround the frame. On the right the hand painted Royal Standard is above a gilt cypher and sprays of flowers. The rear of both has a Union Jack flying from a tasselled staff with "George VI King and Emperor". Handles are pale blue and there are blue and gold lines on the rim.

304   305

*306 One of the most delightful pieces by *Paragon*. This small porcelain coffee can and saucer (6 cms) are completely covered with decoration. The Royal Arms are very heavily enamelled as is the inscription "Dieu et mon Droit". The body is covered with blue, rose and carmine "swirls" creating a most sumptuous effect on this miniature set. The saucer itself is striking, with the large coat of arms and supporting lion and unicorn beautifully adapted to suit the shape. Thick gold bands on the deckled edges of the cup and saucer complete the extraordinarily rich effect. There is a matching Edward piece.

306

*307 A classically simple decoration of light brown profiles within a wreath of green laurel surmounted by a red crown makes this pottery beaker (11.5 cms) a distinguished product of the *Wedgwood* factory. Limited use of colour on the creamware body is wonderfully effective. The beaker here has the coat of arms of Bowdon UDC on the reverse. See also **(R3)**

*308 From *Booths Ltd* comes this barrel-shaped pottery mug (9.5 cms). The portraits are in oval frames of laurel. "Long may they reign" sits above with caption and date beneath. On the reverse a simple commemorative statement. The whole is printed in black which makes for a very dramatic presentation.

307   308

309 310 311

312 313

314 315 316

*309 A multi-colour transfer print of medallion portraits in an oval frame, surrounded by flags, lion, unicorn and national flowers decorate the front of this pottery mug (8 cms) from *Crown Ducal*.

*310 *Tams Ware* produced this attractive, waisted, pottery mug (9.5 cms) with an interesting handle shape. The colourful transfer adopts another "medallions" approach. Around the rim on a yellow band is "King George and Queen Elizabeth Crowned May 12 1937". Inscription on the back shows this was presented by the Mayor of Coventry.

*311 This is the adapted Laura Knight design originally made for Edward VIII. (**N6**), here printed on a *Burleighware* beaker (8 cms). The alternative presentation of a smaller design taking up only some two thirds of the height is visually less satisfactory.

*312 This pottery beaker (11 cms) with a simple, coloured Royal Arms is of interest mainly as having been commissioned by the now-defunct London County Council whose arms appear on the back. Maker, *Wood & Sons*.

*313 *Royal Winton* made this chubby, barrel-shaped mug (9.5 cms). The full colour print has yet another different set of portraits; George is by Vandyk and Elizabeth by Bassano (signatures are below the portraits).

*314, *315, *316 Illustrated here is a representative group from *Paragon*. On the cup and saucer (7 cms) which has a gold lion handle can be seen the reverse decoration whilst the chocolate cup (9.5 cms) on the right also with gold handle shows the front. The plate (22 cms) is smaller than those most frequently found and has a moulded and deckled rim. J.A. Robinson the designer's signature is incorporated.

*317 Loving cups seem to have come into their own in 1937, and here are shown two more typical examples. On the left from *Collingwood* (8.5 cms) is the reverse which has Marcus Adams photographs of the two Princesses. The front is at **(R4)**.

*318 On the right a porcelain example from *Radfords* Crown china (8 cms) has the now familiar Vandyk transfer seen on a number of commemoratives. The handles have moulded and printed crowns and on the reverse a Royal cypher.

317   318

319

*319 Illustrated here is a very unusual three-handled pottery loving-cup (8.5 cms) commemorating the three Kings who reigned in 1936. Between each handle are traditional transfer prints; George V and Queen Mary at their Silver Jubilee, Edward VIII (shown), and George VI and Queen Elizabeth for their Coronation. Inside the rim "The three reigns of nineteen thirty six". Maker, *Bovey* pottery

*320 This art pottery mug comes from the *Moorcroft* factory. Its design, reminiscent of those produced for Edward VII and George V, consists of two concentric bands of deep green separated by one of ivory. A crown decorates the front, a sceptre the back. "King George VI and Elizabeth" the bottom band. Signature of Wm Moorcroft on the base. His stylish work is now very much sought after.

320

Royal Tours and Visits

During the latter half of her reign Queen Victoria lived in comparative seclusion, and while she still took her affairs of state very seriously, for the most part left Albert Edward Prince of Wales, and others, to act as her representative on public occasions. As travelling became easier and the railway system developed more requests were made for royalty to attend public functions both at home and abroad. When Albert Edward became King, his son George, Duke of York assumed greater responsibility in this direction which increased throughout Edward VII's short reign.

The Great War and its aftermath dominated the first ten years of George V's reign, but in the early 20s Edward, Prince of Wales, heir to the throne, embarked on a series of four Dominion tours to Canada, Australia and New Zealand, India and South Africa (341). When Edward became King he was the most travelled monarch reputedly having covered some 300,000 miles in his public duties. His brother Albert (later George VI) had continued a career in the Royal Navy, and later the Air Force, but on becoming Duke of York in 1920 he became more committed to royal duties, which culminated in a tour of New Zealand and Australia (345) in 1927 where he opened the new Federal Capitol in Canberra. Nearer home both the Prince of Wales and the Duke were continually in demand over the ensuing years.

It is not surprising that, with a plethora of royal visits, many should be commemorated on souvenirs of one kind and another.

The list (page 113) is most varied, ranging from a visit to Morley Co-op (352) to the opening of the Australian Federal Parliament (P7), and is far from complete. In spite of extended Dominion tours of the 20s there is a distinct lack of china commemorating these events. Established potters such as Doulton, Shelley and Aynsley had a thriving export business to the Dominions and supplied some pieces direct to their overseas agents, but there can be little doubt that local manufacturers must have copied the essentially English idea of commemorating events on mugs, beakers and the like.

*321 *322 Both sides of this unusual pottery mug (9.5 cm) made by *Maling* are shown, and commemorate the visit made by the Prince of Wales in 1900 to open the Royal Infirmary, Newcastle upon Tyne. Portraits of the Queen and her representative, Edward' appear together with that of an unidentified dignitary and the Arms of Newcastle. A gem for the Maling collectors!

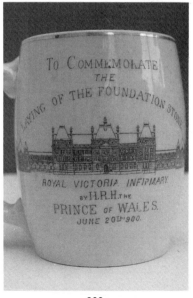

321   322

*323 *324 King George V and Queen Mary made an extensive tour of the Potteries in April 1913 and manufacturers took advantage of the occasion to commemorate the event on some of their wares.

The pottery mug (7 cm) has no manufacturer's back stamp and is an adaptation of a transfer used for the coronation two years earlier. Framed coloured portraits of George and Mary are enhanced by a crown and floral emblems. An inscription in blue ribbon

323   **324**

reads "Queen Mary, King George V Crowned". The reverse bears the arms of the borough of Stoke-on-Trent with the inscription "To commemorate the visit of King George V and Queen Mary to the County Borough of Stoke-on-Trent, April 22nd 23rd 1913. Alderman F. Green J.P. Mayor".

*325 A beaker (9.5 cm) commemorating the same tour, but this time to Leek, was made in pottery by *Bishop and Stonier* (Bisto). The coloured portraits of George and Mary in coronation robes are striking and

325   **326**

were used by the manufacturer on coronation pieces. A simple inscription within a decorated shield records the visit.

*326 *Pearl Pottery* produced this mug recording George V's visit to Frodsham on July 8th 1925. A particularly impressive coloured portrait of George in naval uniform decorates the front

*327 Both the *Doulton* mug (9 cm) and the unmarked tyg (10 cm) commemorate part of the West Country visit made by the Prince and Princess of Wales in June 1909. The green transfer on the mug is similar to that used for their marriage **(201)** in 1893.

327   **328**

*328 Pale green transfer prints of the royal couple, the Bishop of Bath and a view of Glastonbury Abbey decorate the three sides of the tyg (10cms) which is sometimes found in a smaller size and other colours.

329 **330**

*329, *330 Princess Mary, daughter of George V, is particularly remembered for the brass Christmas gift boxes containing tobacco or chocolate which bore her profile, and were widely distributed to the soldiers in France in 1914. She clearly maintained an interest in charities connected with the Great War, as demonstrated by these two memorial pieces.

*331 *332 The earlier mug (8.5 cm) shows a sepia head and shoulder profile with details of a visit to Whitby and District on the reverse. A somewhat more attractive picture of the Princess, again in sepia, decorates the front of the later mug. The more elaborate inscription includes a reference to Castleford Public Market. A retailer's mark for Cloxie & Co, Castleford, is on the base of the mug.

*333 It is not surprising that, in view of Queen Victoria's withdrawal from public functions during the latter half of her reign, items commemorating her visits are not often seen.
This mug (7.5 cm) is made of porcelain and shows on the front a colour transfer

331 **332**

333

"Order of Garter" portrait of Victoria against a pink ground. On the reverse a pale green harp, angel and shamrock are encircled by a similarly coloured inscription commemorating the Queen's visit to Ireland in April 1900. Interestingly, the maker's backstamp has been deliberately erased, though close examination of the shape of the mug, particularly the handle, shows it to be the same as that used by *Doulton* in 1897 **(B6).** The Garter portrait was used extensively, though not exclusively, by Doulton which gives some weight to the argument that they were the manufacturers.

*334 Prince Edward was invested as Prince of Wales at Carnarvon Castle on 13 July 1911. He delighted the Welsh nation by making a speech in their own language, the first Prince of Wales ever to do so. The event was well celebrated on commemorative china, of which this Cardiff mug (7.5 cm) is the best known.

A portrait of Edward in naval uniform dominates the front of the mug. Coloured flags, a harp, the Prince of Wales feathers and suitable inscriptions complete the design. The reverse shows the City of Cardiff arms and is inscribed "Presented by the Lord Mayor, Alderman Charles A Bird, J.P.".

This mug can be found in both pottery and porcelain with the *Royal Winton* back stamp.

334

*335 This attractive pottery plate (19.5 cm) has a blue transfer and records four of the seven names of the Prince within a band encircling his portrait, which in turn is supported by a pair of Welsh dragons. An inscription below records that he was installed at Carnarvon in the coronation year of H.M. George V 1911. There is no potter's mark.

335

*336 A small milk jug (6.5 cm) shows the now familiar black and white portrait of Edward in an oval frame flanked by red dragons. Above the portrait is a Welsh patriotic phrase. The lower inscription reads "Souvenir in commemoration of HRH Prince of Wales, investiture Carnarvon Castle, July 13th 1911". It is more than likely that this jug would have formed part of a teaset including a teapot, cups, saucers and plates.

336

337 338

339 340

341

*337 *339 Two different portraits of Edward in Service uniform are shown here. The first is a *Shelley* pottery mug (7.5 cm) with him in naval uniform. A black and white portrait within a garland of oak and laurel leaves, is surmounted by the Prince of Wales feathers. The reverse shows the borough arms of Whitehaven with a commemorative inscription "A Souvenir of the Royal Visit 1927".

*338 *340 The second mug (7.5 cm) has a large sepia transfer portrait of the Prince in the uniform of the Welsh Guards. On the reverse is the borough coat of arms of Workington and the inscription commemorates the visit on June 30th 1927. It is an unmarked mug made of pottery. This particular portrait is often seen on small pieces of souvenir ware and mostly without a maker's mark or dated inscription.

*341 It was intended that Edward should visit South Africa in 1924, but during the heat of the elections of that year there had been an anti-British feeling among the South African Dutch which caused the visit to be postponed to the following year. He was well recieved by the new Nationalist Government when he subsequently made the visit in 1925.

This souvenir of the visit to Pretoria in June 1925 is in the form of an attractive mug (8 cm) with a large inscription in both English and Afrikaans. One side shows a sepia portrait of the Prince in military uniform, whilst the other has a coloured enamelled coat of arms of Pretoria. It was manufactured by *Pooles,* Longton, Staffs, in bone china. *Shelley* prematurely produced tea ware in anticipation of the tour which was dated a year earlier than the commencement.

*342 *Wilemans* (Foley/Shelley) were responsible for producing some attractive china commemorating royal visits. The two-portrait Foley coronation transfer **(H7)** was used on this mug (7 cm) to mark the visit of Edward VII and Alexandra to open the bridge over the Tyne in July 1906.

It is recorded elsewhere that Edward and Alexandra alighted from their train in the centre of the bridge where Queen Alexandra "released the silken cord stretched across the rails, by pressing an electric button". The royal party then proceeded by train to Alnwick.

342

*343 Almost two years later to the day George, Prince of Wales, attended the Royal Show Newcastle-Upon-Tyne, and *Foley* produced this cup (5 cm) and saucer in their popular Dainty White pattern, to mark the occasion.

Below the Prince of Wales feathers, a transfer of a mythological figure holds a sheaf of wheat and a sickle. A plough and cornucopia complete the design. A pale blue banner below reads "Royal Show Newcastle-on-Tyne July 1908". The three feathers motif is repeated inside the cup.

343

*344 Some 20 years later in October 1928 George V followed his father's footsteps when he returned to Newcastle to open another bridge over the Tyne, and again *Shelley* marked the occasion. This white ground porcelain dish (16 cm) has an unusual moulded design on which is printed a most detailed colour transfer showing the two adjacent bridges over the river.

344

345

346

347

*345 On 6 January 1927 the Duke and Duchess of York left for their Australian tour which was to culminate in the opening of the New Federal Parliament Building in Canberra. After a journey which took them first to Fiji and New Zealand, the Duke delivered his father's message at the opening ceremony exactly 26 years after George had opened the first Federal Parliament **(P5)**.

It is likely that quite a number of souvenirs were made to celebrate the tour, with the majority being on sale in Australia. Burslem potter, *Gater, Hall & Co.* produced the pottery jug (13 cm). The front features a pair of rather unflattering transfer portraits of the Duke and Duchess with inscription against a pale blue enamelled outline of the Australian continent, coloured flags and dove of peace. On the reverse of the jug a patriotic message proclaims "Australia member of the Commonwealth of Nations looks with pride and joy to the homelands in welcoming to her shores the representatives of the British Royal House".

*346 The moulded dish (17cm) shows a good likeness of the royal couple within a pair of decorated oval frames. A single description commemorates the purpose of their visit. There is no maker's mark.

*347 Though there is no inscription other than "Duke and Duchess of Cornwall and York" one might speculate that this teapot commemorates the visit to either Australia or Canada in 1901. The shape is typical of the style of the times. The base and rim of the teapot and lid are decorated in rust coloured bands and the black and white portrait of the Duke and Duchess is less formal than that generally seen. Though there is no maker's mark it is very likely to be of Continental origin.

*348 *Radfords* produced this mug (7.5 cm) for the visit of King George V and Queen Mary to Manchester on July 17 1934. The overall transfer is light brown with appropriate colours for the crown, flags and national emblems. Vignettes showing a lion, tiger, emu and kangaroo together with the names of South Africa, India, New Zealand and Australia decorate the sides.

*349 Royal visits were particularly well received and commemorated in the North East of England. This pottery cup and saucer was made by the local potters *Maling* to commemorate the opening of the North East Coast Industrial Exhibition, Newcastle-upon-Tyne in 1929 by the Prince of Wales and is inscribed as such on the base of both cup and saucer. A black and white transfer printed picture showing the Exhibition buildings, with a pale blue and yellow tinted background, dominate the saucer and this is repeated on the reverse side of the cup. On the front of the cup the Prince of Wales is shown in naval uniform against a pale blue background within a leaf frame. A geometric pattern borders the cup and saucer to complete the decoration. Collectors will be familiar with the somewhat casual portrayal of Edward smoking a cigarette. It was taken from a photograph of Edward signing the visitors' book in Halifax, Nova Scotia, towards the end of his visit to Canada in 1920. Other small souvenir pieces are to be found with the same picture but more often than not without an inscription.

*350 The Prince of Wales was President of the British Empire Exhibition and had been instrumental in finding the guarantee of a fund of £1m for the initial work on the 1924 Exhibition. The mug shows a black and white portrait of the Prince in naval uniform within a simple frame with inscription below.

348

349

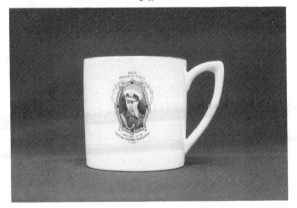

350

351

*351 *Grimwades*, Staffs, manufactured this plate (25.5 cm) to commemorate Edward Prince of Wales' visit to Canada in 1920 and this is recorded on the back of the plate. Edward is shown in grey lounge suit and homberg against a background of maple leaves in fading autumn colours.

He acquired a special affection for Canada and purchased a ranch in Alberta which was made to pay its way, as well as serving as a retreat. He made several private visits to the ranch and maintained an interest in its development.

The Canadian visit was the first of a series of overseas tours made by Edward as the King's representative and was both extensive and exhausting. He travelled from East to West coast taking in most of the principal cities. In Calgary he rode with the cowboys on a 30 mile round-up and became a Tribal Indian Chief at Banff. The zest with which he entered into the numerous ceremonies assured the success of the tour.

*352 This pottery mug would seem to commemorate the visit of the Prince of Wales to the Co-operative Society in Morley, though the visit may have been to the town of Morley and the Co-operative Society took advantage of the opportunity to advertise. A black and white picture of a large corner store appears on the reverse of the mug which has no manufacturer's back stamp.

*353 *Doulton* used one of their standard coronation portrait transfers **(188)** on the front of this pottery mug to commemorate the visit of George V and Mary to Chorley. The reverse shows the arms of the town and details of the event which took place on 10 July 1913.

352

353

*354 An inscription which reads "One King, One flag, One fleet, One Empire" is generally assumed to identify this piece as one made as a souvenir of the review of the fleet. A portrait of Edward in Midshipman's uniform appears between those of his parents. Lithophane examples are also found with this transfer.

*355 The beaker shows another portrait of the young Edward in naval uniform with dominant red Welsh dragons and inscription recording his investiture in Caernarvon, where the first Prince of Wales was created in 1301. It is worthwhile remembering that the heir to the throne does not automatically become Prince of Wales and must await the decision of the monarch.

354   355

There was some reluctance on Edward's part at the time to become Prince of Wales and it is generally believed that King George's motives were purley political and seen as a way to smooth relationships with Lloyd George. Indeed, the Welsh MP's help was enlisted in coaching Edward for the ceremony.

356

*356 On the reverse of this pottery mug is recorded the visit of George V and Mary to Southport. The front shows a fairly common transfer print of them adapted from one produced at the time of the coronation. It is always worth looking on the reverse of what might appear to be a very ordinary piece.

*357 The same transfer has been used by *Doulton* to commemorate this visit to Launceston as that for Newquay (327) and bears the same date. Like so many visit pieces, they were of local interest only and would not have been sold or distributed very widely. Neither of these two *Doulton* commemoratives is easily found.

357

A list of known commemorated tours and visits

Date	Year	Event	Item
23 Mar	1887	Queen Victoria to lay foundation stone of Victoria Law Courts Birmingham	Not known
	1888	Prince and Princess of Wales to Glasgow International Exhibition	jug
16 Jan	1890	Prince and Princess of Wales to Royal Victoria Hospital, Bournemouth	Mug
21 May	1891	Queen Victoria to Derby	Jug (Goss)
10 May	1893	Queen Victoria to open Imperial Institute London	Not known
	1899	Duke and Duchess of York to Southampton	Not known
April	1900	Queen Victoria to Ireland	Mug (Doulton)
20 June	1900	Prince of Wales to lay foundation stone Royal Victoria Infirmary, Newcastle	Mug (Maling)
	1901	Duke and Duchess of Cornwall and York to Canada	Plate + Teapot
9 May	1901	Duke and Duchess of York to Australia. Federation celebrations opening Federal Parliament.	Beaker (Doulton)
13 May	1902	Princess Henry of Battenburg to lay foundation stone at Municipal building, Hereford	Plate (Doulton)
12 May	1903	Edward VII & Alexandra to Holyrood, Edinburgh	Cup & Saucer + Tyg (Doulton)
	1906	Edward VII to opening of extension to Aberdeen University	Plate (Paragon)
11 July	1906	Edward VII to Newcastle and Alnwick to open rail bridge	Mug
7 July	1908	Prince and Princess of Wales to open Stockport Town Hall	Jug
9 July	1908	Edward VII and Alexandra to open Royal Edward Dock, Avonmouth	Plate/Dish (Doulton)
July	1908	Prince of Wales to open Royal Show, Newcastle	Cup and saucer, mug (Foley)
8 June	1909	Prince and Princess of Wales to Newquay	Mug (Doulton)
8 June	1909	Prince and Princess of Wales to Launceston	Mug (Doulton)
22 Jun	1909	Prince and Princess of Wales to Glastonbury	Tyg
19 Sept	1909	Duke of Connaught to Fairford	Cup and Saucer (Savoy)
	1911	George V Presentation of F.A. Cup Sunderland v Preston North End	Plate
13 July	1911	Prince of Wales Investiture, Caernarvon Castle	Various
Dec	1911	George V to India for Delhi Durbar	Plate
22 Apr	1913	George V and Mary to Colclough Works, Staffs.	Plate
23 Apr	1913	George V and Mary visit to Leek	Beaker
22/23 Apr	1913	George V and Mary to Stoke on Trent	Mug
23 Apr	1913	George V to Stoke	Beaker (Bisto)
8 July	1913	George V to Southport	Mug
10 July	1913	George V to Chorley	Mug (Doulton)
25 June	1914	George V and Mary to Shirebrook	Mug
	1920	Prince of Wales to Canada	Plate
	1924	Prince of Wales to South Africa	Mug (Shelley)
	1925	Prince of Wales to Pretoria	Mug
	1925	Prince of Wales to Argentina	Plate
8 July	1925	George V to Frodsham	Mug
	1924/25	Prince of Wales to Wembley Exhibition	Mug
18 Nov	1925	Princess Mary to Whitby War Memorial Hospital	Mug
	1927	Prince of Wales to Canada	Plate (Paragon)
	1927	Prince of Wales to Whitehaven	Mug (Shelley)
	1927	Prince of Wales to Holmrook	Mug (Shelley)
May	1927	Duke and Duchess of York to "The Capitol", Canberra	Cup, saucer, mug (Aynsley)
29 June	1927	Prince of Wales to Egremont	Mug
30 June	1927	Prince of Wales to Workington	Mug
24 Apr	1928	Duke and Duchess of York to Pudsey	Mug
October	1928	George V to open new Tyne Bridge, Newcastle	Dish, Mug (Shelley)
	1929	Prince of Wales to open North East Coast Exhibition	Cup, saucer (Maling)
23 Aug	1929	Princess Mary to Castleford Maternity Home and Public Market	Mug
15 Dec	1933	Prince of Wales to Morley Co-op	Mug
	1934	Duke of Gloucester to Australia	Mug
17 July	1934	George V and Mary to Manchester	Mug
14 Nov	1934	Duke of Kent to Ruardean	Mug
21 Oct	1937	George VI and Elizabeth to Knottingley	Plate

In Memoriams

Throughout the nineteenth century Victorians retained an almost obsessive interest in death, with a whole industry working to satisfy the needs of the bereaved and their families. This sentimentality was responsibility for such things as mourning jewellery which often incorporated locks of hair of the deceased. Periods of deep mourning by close relations were strictly observed and could often be measured in years rather than months. It was a time of mausoleums, eulogies and guardian angels. The death of Charlotte in 1817 was a widely commemorated event reflecting her popularity and items for this event are still to be found at a reasonable price.

Prince Albert's death was a bitter blow to Victoria and left her almost broken hearted. In spite of the fact that he was very well liked and respected, in memoriam items for his death were not plentiful and potters were at pains to emphasise his achievements rather than just his death, possibly influenced by their knowledge of how grief stricken the Queen was.

Victoria's death in 1901 did not bring with it the flood of commemorative china one might have expected considering the vast quantities produced for the Jubilee a few years earlier. It is true to say, however, that Victorians were becoming less obsessed with mourning. Nevertheless in memoriam pieces for Victoria are to be found, with several of the major manufacturers **(363) (380)** producing pieces.

Edward's death was commemorated to about the same extent, again with some principal china manufacturers being involved. These pieces seem to have survived in greater quantities, though they are still comparatively difficult to find.

By the time George VI came to the throne interest in perpetuating the act of mourning had waned considerably and it may be because of this that so few in memoriam pieces were made for his father, George V.

358

359

*358 A finely sculptured head and shoulders portrait of Edward VII in a pale rose colour has been set against a mottled green background on this unusual tile (20 cm). Incised on the back are dates for his birth, reign and death and a manufacturer's back stamp for the *Dicker Pottery,* Sussex.

*359 There are very few items of any kind which commemorate the death of the Duke of Clarence, eldest son of Albert Edward, Prince of Wales. *Doulton* produced this two-tone brown jug (23 cm) which records the date of his death in 1892.

*360 A contemporary portrait of Victoria in sepia is shown on this pottery mug (7 cm) manufactured after her death in 1901. The dates of the start and end of her reign appear either side of a facsimile signature which accompany the words "Queen and Mother". Made by *Chapmans*.

360

361

*361 The reverse of **(360)** shows the round tower at Windsor Castle. One might speculate that this could have been a memento sold locally in the town of Windsor.

*362 This is either a plaque or teapot stand which has fortunately remained in good condition. It shows the popular "Garter" portrait of Victoria set against a green ground, beneath the words "In Memoriam". Further inscriptions record the dates of her birth, accession and death. A smaller inscription also seen on some Jubilee pieces reads "She wrought her people lasting good". The whole plaque is framed by a contrasting dark brown border. Manufacturer *Grimwades*.

362

*363 *Doulton* produced some tastefully designed in memoriam items for Victoria. The "Garter" portrait first used by them for the Diamond Jubilee features again, but inscriptions and patterned decorations are in purple. This one shows a small porcelain plate with a place for the cup offset to the side. A similar arrangement was used by *Foley* for one of their Diamond Jubilee pieces and the idea has been repeated a number of times since. Inscriptions record the date of her birth and death and declare that "she wrought her people lasting good". Both rims are gilded and have a purple decorated border.

363

*364 The same decorations and inscriptions used on (363) appear on this small attractive porcelain *Doulton* tyg (8.5 cm). The handles are delicately moulded and have some gilding.

*365 One of the more interesting plates (23.5 cm) for the death of Edward VII was made by *Winton*. Large coloured head and shoulder portraits of Edward and Alexandra in coronation robes are shown in oval frames with that of Edward outlined in black. Flags and emblems form a suitable background, a ribbon inscripton below states "Enthroned in the hearts of their people". A further printed inscription reads "The Queen Mother, may heaven comfort her".

364

365

366

*366 This shows a second side of the *Doulton* mug (M5) which records the dates of Victoria's birth, accession, coronation and death, below a crown and the words "In loving and loyal remembrance of her most gracious majesty, Queen Victoria".

The third side shows a book within a laurel leaf frame. Below a specially composed poem by Tennyson reads "Her court was pure, her life serene, God gave her peace, her land reposed. A thousand claims to reverence closed. In her as mother, wife and Queen". All inscriptions are in purple.

367   **368**

*367, *368 Edward VII was labelled "A Peacemaker" on many of his in memoriam pieces, and this appears on both this plaque (25 cm) and the mug (11 cm).

The pottery plaque has a large blue transfer print of him in uniform and records the dates of his birth and death. Similarly, the mug records these dates, but shows a coloured portrait. Neither has a manufacturer's backstamp.

369

*369 Close examination reveals this pottery mug (7.5 cm) to be unusual.

A sepia transfer print shows Edward's portrait framed below a crown. Ribbon inscriptions record dates of his birth and death, confirming it to be an in memoriam piece.

However, printed at the base is the inscription "Dudley and District Children's Gala 1910".
Local references are common on Jubilee and Coronation wares but celebrating a children's gala at the same time as mourning a King does seem to be somewhat incongruous.

*370 Very few examples of in memoriam pieces for George V seem to turn up and one must assume that little was made to commemorate the occasion. This pottery plaque (23 cm) is a delightful tribute to the "Sailor King" and shows him at the helm of a sailing ship. It is fashioned in low relief in colours of pale cream and brown, with broad bands of leaves and fruit on the rim. "Georgius V Rex 1910-36" is inscribed at the top of the plaque. There is no maker's stamp.

370

371

*371, *372 Doulton manufactured this large pottery loving cup (12 cm) using the same head and shoulders portrait of George as that for the Jubilee (215) a year earlier.

The sepia portrait is framed in a garland of leaves in low relief within simple inscriptions above. There are narrow silver bands to upper and lower rims.

372

On the reverse a sepia printed tribute reads "The friend of his people; so long as the history of the British Empire is written his reign will be recorded with gratitude. 1910-1936". This piece is often called the "Exemplar loving cup".

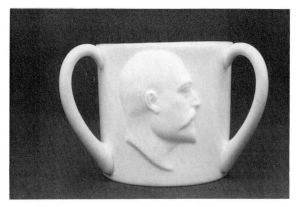

373

*373 This large profile in relief of Edward VII is seen on a fine porcelain *Goss* tyg (8 cm). The second side bears an enamelled coat of arms of Exmouth where it was probably ordered by a local retailer.

374   375

*374 The remaining side of the tyg is shown with the enamelled coat of arms of Edward dominating. Yet again, Edward is referred to as "Peacemaker" with accompanying dates for his birth, accession and death.

*375 A model of a Roman urn found in Chichester and made by *Goss* shows another framed profile of Edward with the same transfer inscription as the tyg.

376

*376 A small central portrait of Edward with the same colour transfer as used on a mug (368) appears on this pottery plate (22 cm). The body of the plate is slightly ribbed with a scalloped border highlighted in gold. Inscriptions are the same as those on the mug and there is no manufacturer's backstamp.

*377 Collectors of *Crown Devon* pottery would be pleased to have this loving cup (8.5 cm) made by *Fielding & Co.* A simple but effective black transfer shows a framed portrait of Edward which itself is partly framed with a leaf design and inscriptions. The reverse records the dates of his birth, marriage, coronation and death. Rims and handles have thin silver coloured bands.

377

*378 J. A. Robinson *(Arcadian China)* made this pretty porcelain cup (6 cm) and saucer for Edward VII's death. A coloured enamel portrait of Edward is surrounded by coloured printed inscriptions recording dates of his birth, accession and death. The crinkled edges of both cup and saucer are decorated in gold.

*379 There is no maker's mark on this in memoriam mug (8 cm) for Edward VII. A very pale black transfer of Edward and Alexandra is shown on this traditional shape and a large inscription in gold around the upper outside rim reads "In memory of King Edward VII".

378   379

*380 No prizes for recognising this so familiar barrel shape mug (9.5 cm) produced by the *Maling* factory.
A coloured transfer printed portrait of Victoria appears below coloured crossed flags surmounted by a crown and the whole is interspersed with sprays of forget-me-nots. The rim is decorated with a thin gold band and the inscription in black reads "In memory of our beloved Queen Victoria, 1837 - 1901".

380

"The Empire's little Princesses"

Princess Elizabeth was born on April 21st 1926 at 17 Bruton St. London, and Princess Margaret on August 21st 1930 at Glamis Castle (the London and Scottish homes of their Maternal grandparents - the Earl and Countess of Strathmore). Their parents were still, at the time, Duke and Duchess of York and although carrying out some Royal engagements, they were very much less in the public eye than the Prince of Wales. They preferred the relatively private, family life. In 1926 there was not the slightest hint of the enormous change in status that was to befall the Duke of York's family. Edward, Prince of Wales was only 32 and was confidently expected to marry and have a family of his own.

The Yorks were popular and in particular the country "took" to the two young princesses. Commemorative items had been issued to mark their births (Q2 Q3) and further items appeared from time to time. After the difficulties of the Abdication there was a swell of popular approval for George VI and his family who had so unexpectedly been thrown into the limelight, and large numbers of souvenirs were produced featuring the two princesses, most based on a series of charming photographs taken by Marcus Adams. Paragon again issued a range (Q10) as did Doulton (383), Grafton (Q4) and Crown Ducal (385). These attractive souvenir pieces are much sought after by collectors.
The princesses also featured on many of the Coronation commemoratives; Wedgwood & Co (294), Shelley (298). In his Abdication speech, Edward VIII said of George VI that he "has one matchless blessing shared by so many of you and not bestowed on me - a happy home with his wife and children."

Certainly the providers of commemorative items of all kinds were not slow to capitalise on this thought, and the Royal Family appeared on every conceivable souvenir.

381   382

*381, *382 These matched, tapering porcelain mugs (8 cms) from *Royal Doulton*, show the delightful Marcus Adams studies of Princess Elizabeth and Princess Margaret Rose. The portraits are printed in light sepia within green frames and laurel leaves. The rims are gilded on the insides.

383   384

*383, *384 The reverse of the design has inscriptions, illustrated here on a pair of matching tall mugs (9.5 cms) in fine porcelain from *Royal Doulton*. The acknowledgement "from a photograph by Marcus Adams" is on the base of all the items together with the Royal Doulton mark. These were produced in at least three different shapes of mug all of which are now difficult to find.

*385, *386 A pair of matching, pottery mugs (7.5 cms) from *Crown Ducal* feature only the heads of the two princesses (again from photographs by Marcus Adams). Printed in light brown, the large portraits strike a very appealing note. The titles "Princess Elizabeth" and "Princess Margaret Rose" are printed inside the mugs and on the respective bases "Born April 21st 1926", "Born August 21st 1930". The rims, bases and handles are embellished with gilding

385   386

*387, *388 The same transfer-printed design is featured on these two cups and saucers. On the left, the porcelain set from *Colclough* china (7 cms), shows both princesses on the saucer with Princess Elizabeth alone on the cup. (Would there be a matching set with Princess Margaret?). On the right the set here is in pottery (7 cms) and unmarked. Both princesses are shown on the cup with a plain saucer. All the portraits are printed in dark brown within a green frame and surrounded by national flowers "Photograph by Marcus Adams" is printed beneath the portraits.

387   388

389   390   391

*389, *390, *391 Many items of tableware featuring the two princesses were produced in 1936/37 and illustrated here are three examples of the "cheap and cheerful" variety. The pottery egg cup shows Princess Elizabeth whilst the doll's tea-set cup saucer and milk jug each depict Princess Margaret Rose.

Five Popular Potteries

We have included colour illustrations of selections from five major potteries whose commemorative wares have consistently been of special interest and quality, and which are today keenly sought after by collectors. Of course there are fine items from other potteries such as Minton, Wm Lowe, Copeland, Goss, Wedgwood Worcester etc and examples of these are illustrated elsewhere. The limitations of space necessitated a difficult choice. The following pages provide a little background information on our selected potteries which we trust will help increase the collector's enjoyment and appreciation.

AYNSLEY

From an interest which started as a hobby, John Aynsley started a family business which was to last for some 200 years. He was a mining engineer by profession and, having moved to Longton to take charge of a local colliery, became increasingly interested in pottery making in his spare time. In 1775 he took the unusual step of establishing himself as a master potter working from his own small factory in Longton.

His early products consisted mainly of jugs for beer and cider, which he cleverly decorated himself with engravings of sporting, humourous and political events of the day. These were the forerunners of commemorative china which the company was to continue to produce throughout its long history.

As the factory prospered in the hands of John's son and later his grandson, the quality of their wares improved and they gained a reputation as manufacturers of bone china of the very highest quality.

Queen Victoria selected Aynsley china for use on the royal yacht HMS Osborne and, more recently, an Aynsley pattern was selected by Princess Elizabeth for her wedding present of 240 pieces from the British Ceramic Manufacturers Federation on the occasion of her marriage of her marriage to Prince Philip in 1947.

Collectors are particularly attracted to Aynsley commemoratives by the remarkably fine quality of their china, coupled with the distinctive designs. The portrait version cup and saucer for Victoria's Diamond Jubilee was produced in several different pastel shades against a white ground, and a delightful version with gold decoration (D7) is also seen. Surprisingly, nothing seems to have been made for the Golden Jubilee in 1887, and though there is a dearth of quality pieces for this event, one would have expected Aynsley to have made a contribution.

A mixture of coats of arms and portraits were favoured for later events and made in mugs, cups and saucers, plates and jugs (Plate D) with several interesting designs for the back decorations (126) (293). Aynsley have proved to be one of the most long-lasting manufacturers of commemorative wares, continuing to maintain a high standard of design and quality.

PARAGON

The name Paragon was used as a trade name and was incorporated into their back stamp by the Star China Co. Longton, Staffs, when they were established in 1900. In or around 1920 the Company became known as the Paragon China Co Ltd.

The first "By Appointment" back stamp appeared in the early thirties with reference first to Queen Mary and her daughter-in-law Queen Elizabeth, and later the present Queen. Paragon later became part of the Doulton group of companies.

For collectors of royal commemoratives the mug for George V (J7) is an early example of the company's products. The Great War afforded them the opportunity to produce a patriotic series showing national flags of the Allies, but their first notable contribution to the royal commemorative market was the china tea service for the birth of Princess Elizabeth (Q1). This was followed by one for the birth of Princess Margaret Rose (Q3) and souvenirs of the royal children from photographs by Marcus Adams (Q7). More was to follow, but in a different vein, with lavish use of enamelling and gilding, ornate handles to the mugs and loving cups (E3), coupled with the armorial designs of J.A. Robinson. Paragon is now a firm favourite with collectors, not only because of the obvious quality of their wares, but for the variety of shapes and sizes which were made; a freedom unlikely to be allowed by present day manufacturers.

DOULTON

John Doulton entered into partnership in a small pottery in Vauxhall Walk in Lambeth in 1815, having served an apprenticeship at the nearby Fulham Pottery.

The principal products of the Vauxhall factory, trading under the name of Doulton & Watts, were salt glazed jugs, bottles, ink pots and the like but, as the firm expanded, so did the range of products to include a few political commemorative items. Most popular were the Reform flasks and bottles of 1832 and later a gin flask and mug to celebrate Queen Victoria's accession.

By 1850 the company was completely owned by Doulton & Sons, and John's son Henry, who had joined the firm in 1835 as an apprentice, was taking an increasingly active role in running the business. He was particularly interested in the Arts, giving support to the Lambeth Art Studios and employing some of their students.

In 1860 the foundation stone of the new Vauxhall premises was laid by the Prince of Wales, heralding a royal patronage which was to last a further fifty years.

In spite of Henry's active encouragement of the Arts, the staple product of the factory was still for building and electrical engineers and it was not until 1870 that Doulton made a somewhat tentative step towards the production of the now famous Lambeth Art pottery.

Within a decade Henry Doulton entered into a partnership with the well established Pinder Bourne & Co in Burslem, Staffordshire, and were soon rivalling Worcester and Derby for their finely painted wares.

The two 1887 jubilee mugs (32) (33) and subsequently all pottery and porcelain commemoratives were produced at Burslem, whilst all stoneware was made at the Lambeth factory until its close in 1956. Under Henry Doulton's inspiration the Company's products continued to gain respect in the industry culminating in the award of the Albert Medal of the Society of Arts to Henry Doulton in 1885, personally bestowed by the Prince of Wales. Henry was further honoured in 1887 when he received a Knighthood from Queen Victoria.

It is not surprising that, with Henry Doulton's creativity and foresight, and the particular interest shown by the Prince of Wales, royal commemorative wares were to be a strong feature of their factories' products.

The 1897 Jubilee and Edward VII's Coronation in 1902 were two events to which Doulton made the greatest and most varied contributions. Some idea of the range of items produced from 1887 to 1953 can be gauged by an exhibition staged by the Royal Doulton International Collectors Club in 1984/5 where some 300 different Doulton Burslem royal commemoratives were on view, the majority of which came from the Titmuss collection. Indeed, the attraction of Doulton commemoratives lies particularly in the seemingly endless variety of shapes (R7), sizes and colours (F5) (F8) that were produced. One can only assume that every encouragement was given to the designers to experiment, and the degree of freedom they enjoyed resulted in some fine and unusual pieces for today's collectors.

Special commissions were popular for municipal boroughs (F2) (188) and, though we can only guess the numbers produced, it is likely that the 'run' was not less than 500. In the case of all stoneware products, because of the work involved, probably not more than 2.000 would have been made in total. Some pieces were made in small numbers catering for the more expensive end of the market, often attracting the attention of principal designers such as Robert Allen (front cover) and John Broad (27). Births (212) deaths (M5) (359) marriages (K6) and visits (P6) (333) were also commemorated, produced in smaller numbers, and are now particularly sought after by collectors.

HAMMERSLEY

In 1887 the Hammersley Company started trading from Alsager Pottery, Longton, Staffordshire, and quickly established a reputation for the production of finely decorated porcelain tea ware. Like most principal potteries they produced a variety of items to commemorate royal events which soon became popular with discerning collectors.

With very few exceptions (265) these were made in porcelain to a very high standard of workmanship, with designs based on enamelled flags, coats of arms and national emblems, rather than portraits of the monarchs. One notable exception was for the 1897 jubilee with the letters VR (G6) replaced by a coloured Garter Sash portrait of Victoria against a very similar background.

A surprising feature of the 1897 design **(G7)** is the use of the wrongly coloured Union Jack in what is otherwise a particularly pleasing composition. The company became part of the Worcester Spode group in 1976.

FOLEY/SHELLEY

The Company of James Wileman became established potters in the Foley area of Longton, Staffordshire, around 1865 and entered into partnership with Joseph Shelley in 1872. Within ten years Joseph's son Percy had joined the firm and a few years later the Shelley family became sole owners of the pottery. Though Percy lacked any formal training in the trade he showed initiative and flair which quickly enhanced the reputation of the company. New artists and modellers were engaged and a thriving export business was developed in Australia, Cananda and the U.S.A.

The name of Wileman had been retained but 'Foley' had been added to the backstamp on their products. This led to an objection by Brain & Co, a close neighbour, who had also been trading under the 'Foley' name. An ensuing court case resulted in Wileman losing the exclusive right to the use of the 'Foley China' backstamp. The family name was subsequently used, but during a transition period lasting till around 1916 their wares carried the name 'Late Foley, Shelley'. Brain continued to trade as 'Foley China' and produced some royal commemoratives **(249)**. The collector should be careful not to confuse the two companies.

The first royal event commemorated by Wilemans appears to be for 1887 **(H3)**, followed by the Silver Wedding of the Prince of Wales **(K1)**, the 1897 Jubilee and the marriage of George and May **(199)**.

By the time of Victoria's Diamond Jubilee Wileman's, no doubt encouraged by their earlier successes, showed a firm commitment toward souvenir wares, and indeed later became one of the principal producers of crested china. A year earlier they had launched their now famous Dainty White range featuring fluted panels and scalloped edges, and this formed the basic design for many of their commemorative pieces **(M6)**

Wilemans were clearly confident that their contribution would be popular with the public and this is reflected in the number of variations of shape which were made. Six different designs of cups and saucers have so far been recorded, repeated in two sizes, and these can be most easily identified by the shape of the cup handles. Two teapots **(53) (H6)** seen together with jugs, plates and bowls suggest that at least two complete tea sets of different shapes were made. The 1897 enamelled transfer incorporating the royal standard flanked by a lion and unicorn has proved particularly popular with collectors and makes a most impressive display as a collection.

Coats of arms again featured for Edward VII's coronation but a second design was also used showing portraits of Edward and Alexandra. **(H7)** Some very collectable miniature pieces can also be found.

Similarly, two alternative designs were available for George V's coronation in 1911 **(J3) (166)** with two slightly different versions of the portrait of George. For the Silver Jubilee in 1935 a somewhat simplified version of the previous portraits pattern appeared **(H5)** with a thin silver coloured rim on the mugs, beaker and cups.

The following year preparations began for Edward VIII's coronation and Shelley, true to tradition, were quick to meet the public demand for commemorative china for the occasion. Many different shapes were made in both porcelian and pottery, including a large teapot.

Following the abdication of Edward VIII a new design was quickly produced bearing some similarity to that for Edward. Two sizes of loving cup were made with portraits of the princesses on the reverse. Portraits of George VI and Elizabeth and the two children were incorporated into a design for two large plates **(298)**. They are particularly striking and must be amongst the best examples of their kind for this event. A pottery lamp base with shade and a musical jug were interesting additions to the line.

Shelleys reputation for fine china and their continued interest in the souvenir trade prompted many special commissions. Several royal visits **(342) (343)** were commemorated in Shelley china and are much appreciated by collectors for their quality and rarity.